A Surge

PETRIFIED
Flowers

JOIYA MORRISON-EFEMINI

PETRIFIED FLOWERS by Joiya Morrison-Efemini

ANAIAH SURGE
An imprint of ANAIAH PRESS, LLC.
7780 49th ST N. #129
Pinellas Park, FL 33781

First Anaiah Surge print edition June 2020

Edited by Lisa Dunn
Book Design by Anaiah Press
Cover Design by Laura Heritage

Anaiah
Press
Books that inspire

This book is dedicated to my children. There is so much I've forgotten about being a kid. I could not write children well without being surrounded by you, without having been apprenticed by you, and humbled by you. You make me laugh, cry, bite my tongue, and pray more fervently than ever before. Thanks for making Mommy a better child of God.

ACKNOWLEDGEMENTS

To My God: Psalm 63: 3–4 — Your unfailing love is better than life itself; how I praise you! I will praise you as long as I live, lifting up my hand to you in prayer.

To Efe: For your provision, your hard work, and infinite generosity. We don't tell you enough; cannot begin to repay you, for this beautiful life you have given us, by His hand.

To EAE: I will always love you. Not matter what. I look up to you so much for your steadfast determination and the way you push past your comfort zone, even as a natural creature of habit. You have such a kind heart. Always remember to be strong and courageous.

To TPE: I will love you forever and always. No matter what. I love your intelligent mind, your wit, and your generous nature. Remember to put on the FULL ARMOR of God every single day, and to fight against the evil one who wishes to destroy with temptation. Be On Guard!

To ZJE: I love you unconditionally, eternally. No matter what. I'm convinced that God gave me your name. You are a radiant light. NEVER LET ANYONE snuff out that light. It is of God. Use it for His purposes.

To TAE: My love for you is forever. Nothing can stop it. No matter what. You are so, so tenacious. You have your own opinions and your own way of doing things. Make sure to always align your will with the will of God. Your ferocity makes you an invaluable soldier in God's army.

To Mom and Dad: Just thank you, again, forever and ever! Mom, you'll be pleased to read that I have given the Flower Sisters some mischief, as you suggested. And, Dad, you never know how the stories you tell will impact your children—the opening stanza with the one-sided rain came from a story you told me long ago.

To Nicole and Eric: Still the best brother/sister duo I could ask for. Thank you for your prayers, jokes, songs, dances, inspiration, and unconditional love.

To Shaniya: We're so blessed that God decided the Morrisons needed to be a quintet. Always remember who you are. Trust God and rely on Him. And, forgive people.

To my Girlfriends: Thank you for PRAYER. For Truth. For accountability. For laughter and unconditionally love. Thank you for empathy. Thank you for forgiveness. The miles. The memories. The meltdowns. All the times we've "lived together." I look forward to being eighty with you ladies!

To KBS: Your love is boundless. Your support to me has been enthusiastic and steadfast. Your generosity is incalculable. You are gorgeous—inside and out. Your laughter is contagious! You have this gift of showing people, through your eyes, what God intends for them to be. Your heart is truly of Him.

To Jen and Anna: Your contributions—from reading PF, start to finish, several times, and making me fully develop Liam, to writing my query letter for me. I could not have written Iris' story without the two of you. I appreciate you and our little writing group; for the fascinating stories and poems (and struggles) you entrust me with, and for your honest, insightful feedback. Thank you.

To Winnie: Forever grateful.

To the Baileys: For inspiration. I've sprinkled you in here, and I hope you enjoy what you read.

To LISA DUNN: It's one thing to conceive a story. It's quite another thing to come in later, and to raise it. With honesty, wisdom, and meticulous scrutiny, you loved PF as if it was your very own. You grew this story to its full fruition. You are an answer to prayer.

PETRIFIED FLOWERS

DISSIPATION

The afternoon
it rained on their side of the street
but not ours
Dahlia and I sat idle,
too hot to breathe
fully.

We straddled a seesaw,
fixed—

Me digging my flip flop heels
into recycled rubber.
Her suspended mid-air,
defying gravity.

The two of us panting and dripping
at Brooks Street Park.

Wishing we could beam ourselves
thirteen blocks north
to Spriggs Park
where our sisters played.

Wishing we could dip our toes into homemade concrete
and melt into abandon
with the rest of the Flowers.

We had disregarded Mom's orders
to remain inside.
Dahlia was supposed to be confined to her bed.

I'd been roped into nursing her flu.
Instead, we persisted —

I in reclaiming the childhood that had abruptly ended
and Dahlia in growing up.

We played
Bubble Gum, Bubble Gum.
I was too old for the game, but not for the wishing.
If wishing could actualize
the sweet, juicy pieces
we sang of,
maybe we could sing Daddy back
and exhume Mom.
But, our voices cracked
from singing too long.
Our expectations ran dry
from hoping too hard.

Then we heard a murmuring. *Hope.*

We both stopped singing
squinted up
out
over
to the other side of the street.

A miraculous
liquid sheet descended.

Conditions

shifted
immediately.

We seized scanty drafts in fits and waves;
even still, we accepted the
remainders
of their respite
from the unbearable hot spell.

It literally rained on only one side of the street.

The injustice fumed.
Steam surged from the concrete as it poured—
gloriously commonplace.

Acrid on parched tongues
the immoral aftertaste of so many entitlements
permitted just over there.

We weathered still.
Bystanders cemented
on the outskirts of beautiful lives.

GREENER GRASS

Across the street
Monday through Friday
fancy cars dropped off uniformed clones in overpriced
shoes
that strode,
their backs to us,
through the gilded gate
and the massive double doors,
and disappeared
entirely from sight.

Liam
obligingly
described a land where
books were new,
everyone had a computer,
teachers sang their lessons and
danced when students earned A's.

Ceilings didn't leak,
and parents could rush straightaway
when nurses decided
to banish
sick kids.

Every day, the lunch ladies served seven different entrees
and three different desserts.

On our side of the street
we had cars, too.
But mostly
we walked or biked or took the bus to
school,
church.

To grocery stores,
to buy only exactly what Mom wrote on the list,
no matter how tenacious the Littles were
with their begging.

We took the Littles to parks,
grudgingly played dolls with them,
absent-mindedly colored with them.
We read books with them.
All the time thinking how dumb
the dolls and the juvenile books
and the coloring were.

Biology harped on us
to distance ourselves
from childish things,
to seek out and to cleave to
peers,
to roll our eyes,
sigh heavily
and often,
exasperated with everything about the world.

We were in that middle place;

We were supposed to requisition our right to boycott responsibility.

But also,
we elder Flowers were cast away.
Hostages to obligation,
we had no choice but to
hurdle adolescence
and belly flop into young adulthood.

Name-brand cereal was extravagant,
but parks were free,
so we took them.

Parks where most everyone survived
just like us—
dressed in ill-fitting donations
and faded hand-me-downs.

If Liam had asked,
lies would have been more believable
than the truth.

Two years after being transported to the poor side of the street,
we still couldn't fathom the universe in which we were supposed to grow.

A universe
where kids were educated with duct-taped books,
out-of-date,

6

harbored with cockroaches, sheltered beneath leaky roofs,
terrified of getting sick,
of staying whole school days on nurses' cots;
we dreaded the humiliation of being sent
back to class,
walking home,
riding the bus,
sick.
Because no one could
or no one would
pick you up.

We played
touch ball
kickball
basketball
soccer.
Gaga ball
four square
double dutch.

We tagged one another
with hands and
labels—
the shadow
the loudmouth
the bully
the cheater
the Ride-or-Die kid
the Hit-and-Run

the standout—
And roasted one another accordingly.

We,
always bunched together,
had been
The Flower Sisters.
We became
The Fair Weather Flowers.
It only stung
when it was jeered
by someone we'd abandoned.
Like Hakim.

ANTICS

Just a block from Brooks Street,
you could turn left onto Daniels.

On Daniels Street
at the end of a long driveway,
a rickety glass-paneled garage
owned by old Mr. Daniels,
who hated kids,
slumped.
Mr. Daniels shouted at us
and swore when we touched his grass
or his driveway
or if he saw us looking at his garage.

But Mom he whistled at.
Called her *my dark chocolate delight.*
Mom warned us to stay away from
that crazy man
and never to set foot on his property.

The Standouts would wait for him
just at the edge of his lawn,
spit their gum in his grass,
brandish their middle fingers,
gyrate their bottoms and pump their crotches,
their fearlessness fueled by fist bumps
and spectators' laughter.

He'd dart from his garage,
waving a hammer
or broom
or I guess
whatever
he'd been holding
when their antics lit his temper.

The Standouts taunted from a distance
but ran when things got hot.
Only the Ride-or-Dies waited.
The most savage kids,
with Freesia's crush
Darius in command,
would keep laughing
waving
spitting
fist bumping
until Mr. Daniels got right up to them.
Then they would jump off the curb
separating his property from the road
and just stand there,
daring him to claim the street as well.

Mr. Daniels would stop,
toes in perfect alignment with that curb,
never over.

He'd stare at them,
chest heaving,
sweat glazing his rippled forehead,

nose, and neck.
His eyes wished them dead.

Amaryllis said
there was an invisible force field
Mr. Daniels couldn't escape.
She actually felt sorry for him.

Mr. Daniels never left that property line
on foot.
It was always by car.
And every afternoon when he left,
every kid at Brookstreet Housing
invaded his driveway.

One day Hakim proposed a race.
He was always trying to beat somebody
and had smoked all of us
one-by-one
in head-to-head challenges.
But now Hakim offered a chance.

We couldn't beat him, but someone
could beat everyone else.
So many kids signed up
for the chance to take second place,
Hakim had to organize heats.

Freesia and I agreed.
We Flowers would race.
If not, the other kids would call us

scary—
Brookstreet Housing code for
scaredy-cat—
or sneer that we were *too good*
to sweat with the rest of them.
Mr. Daniels never came back
once he left for the day,
and we were sure
Mom had class after work.

Zinnia was the only Flower that made it
into Hakim's heat.
I was glad one of us did,
especially after Azalea crossed her name off the list
angrily when she saw the line ups.
Everyone knows I'm faster than Zin!
Freesia got into the same heat as Darius.
Amaryllis and I preferred to watch.
Dahlia whined that she was with all the *babies*
and proceeded to come in last
amongst all those babies.

On the final race,
which Hakim called
the elite heat,
they set up eight across.
Like all the other groups,
they'd be running from the sidewalk
straight down the driveway
to Mr. Daniels's garage.
The start and finish lines

had been marked in bright red
sidewalk chalk.
Dahlia blew the whistle.

Zinnia had her cheeks puffed round
and her eyes popping out
like she wasn't planning to breathe
for the entire sprint.

Hakim was a cheetah—
sleek and boundless.
His polished skin
black as the cat's glistening spots.
Flashy clothes
and bright red tennis shoes.
Way too expensive for a housing project kid.

He smiled even when he ran.
He wasn't even trying.
Hakim winning by a long shot.
Hakim not stopping in time.
Hakim's arms smashing straight through
a glass panel
on Mr. Daniels' ancient garage.
Hakim's smile distorting,
deforming into a grimace.
Blood outlining the shards of glass
jutting like saber teeth
from the window frame.
Hakim squirting blood all over the driveway,
all over his shirt,

all over his shorts,
and his brand new tennis shoes.

The vermillion sneakers,
upscale and misplaced
on our side of the street,
splattered with
the blood of a black boy.
Stains that rendered them disposable.

Some kids ran to Hakim's Mama.
Some kids stood staring
or crying.
Other kids ran to him,
suddenly bare chested,
wrapped his arms with their shirts,
tried to calm him down.

The six of us ran home.

We weren't even supposed to be out playing
with those kids
in that driveway.
That's how we were branded
The Fair Weather Flowers.
Hakim burned us with it.

After that,
Hakim wouldn't talk to us except
to roast us,
Zinnia worst of all.

And no one in the neighborhood trusted us.

But having sisters is fire-proof insulation.
And we had Liam.

BAE

Liam came to us
and unabashedly conformed
like Laurie to the March Sisters.
It was a slow-motion movie entrance;
permagrin, whole arm wave, skip to his step,
when he showed up.

He was always bringing something for one of us—
a book, a game, candy from another country.
He hungrily accepted
any trivial gift one of The Littles
passed to him.

Mostly, Liam found us at Brooks Street Park.

On the day of the one-sided rain,
we were scattered flowers,
some of us here,
some of us there,
which was rare
and dangerous.

When Liam rounded the corner,
his hair was darkened and curled
by the rain.
His t-shirt clung to him
in polka dots.
He grinned and sauntered

16

down Brooks Street
through the rain
that stopped short of refreshing us.
Liam took some of the sting out,
but the burn still scarred.

I just came from your sisters.
He looked at me.
Thought you might need this.
He handed Dahlia a paper bag,
still looking at me.

I pushed off the ground purposefully
with my legs
and levitated
so that Dahlia could touch down,
climb off.

Thanks!
She looked up at him,
reverent
after peering into the bag.
I would not be privy to her prize;
knew without asking
that she would insist on the secret.
I would find out later, of course.
On her terms.
Because she was only six
and fickle.
She tucked the treasure
under her slight brown arm.

17

From the seesaw
we walked over to the
shade of the pavilion.
I let Dahlia lay her body across
a picnic table.
As long as you hang your feet over the side.
She fell asleep in minutes,
alerting me to check her forehead
to see if she was feverish again.
Her skin felt like raw chicken.

Minutes of stiff silence surrounded
Liam and me.
And then he pulled a tennis ball from his pocket.
Wanna throw?

By then the rain on the other side
had stopped.

The breeze that held its hand
stood still.
Liam's hair glistened auburn again,
still curly from the rain

but lighter,
single tufts waving in the breeze.

I tossed the tennis ball
to him
leisurely

18

between catches
back and forth,
unnerved by
the splattered freckles
across his nose and cheeks
and the way he stared me down
straight to my mind.
He caught the ball without even looking at it,
instantly depleted my brain of the myriad
of topics I'd come up with
while
watching TV,
folding clothes,
listening to music,
staring at teachers in class,
washing dishes,
always thinking of Liam
when he wasn't around.

Freesia would have brought up the rain
and tricked him somehow
into admitting he hadn't even noticed.
I was glad she wasn't there
to challenge him,
and I wished that she was
to make conversation.

I looked around between throws.
Liam and I were the oldest
at the park.
A bunch of housing project kids,

19

like my sisters and me,
mostly doing a whole bunch
of nothing, just like us.
They'd escaped stifling apartments
too puny to run through,
only to suffocate outside.

The tranquility was shattered
by a group
of older kids,
almost grown,
stampeding into the park
shouting and laughing,
cussing and pushing
all the way to the basketball court,
where the little kids tossing airballs
stood no chance
man-to-man
against bullies two and a half times their size.

In the time it takes to shoot a free throw,
the unchallenged victors
had commandeered the cracked and faded court,
and even had the nerve to make fun of the
the flatness of the ball,
their plunder.

Even in my disgust,
their parade captivated me.

Freesia said SWAG was

Something We All Got

and it differentiated
us from them.
Back then, to Freesia
everything was Black and White.

Native Americans have it too.
Swagger is what made white men so jealous
they wanted to destroy us.
We're strong and beautiful;
it scared them.
So they tried to make us feel
weak and ugly.
They're still trying…

I couldn't counter her theory.
I didn't have a better one.
But I didn't agree that only
Blacks and Native Americans had it.
Liam had it too.

A presence that makes you think
he thinks he's all that,
but then you realize
he's just being himself
and he is all that.

At Brooks Street Housing,
Liam was just another white boy.

21

But he was our white boy.
All the regulars knew him.
They roasted him
and they roasted us
because of him.
They were jealous of him;
mostly they ignored him.

But the rowdy teens
who slept in Brooks Street Housing
and ran the streets at night
were unpredictable.
Brooks Street Park was not their normal chill spot.
Seeing them
unnerved me.
Liam might not be safe on Brooks Street
if those boys planned to hang around.

Cops didn't cruise in unmarked cars
down Brooks Street, and around the corner
onto Brookside Drive
with eyes and ears that fabricated
mischief
and trouble
when they saw kids who were
just walking home
half as much in summertime
as they did
when Brookside Academy was in session.

The scholars of Brookside Academy

were safely tucked away
in better parts of the city
or traveling the world
or enriching themselves at sleep-away camps
with horses and tents and lakes
and robots and foreign languages.

I had seen one cruiser that whole day.
It was marked
and going too fast to be monitoring our well-being.

You should get going.
I wouldn't have suggested it if Freesia had been there.
Liam took a furtive glance toward the court.
He shook his head and tossed the ball back to me.
Liam shrugged the danger off.

I'm good. I don't have to be home 'til six.

Spriggs Park was safer for Liam,
but Dahlia was too weak to walk
those six blocks.
Even Brooks Street Park was a risk
when we were supposed to be in our apartment.

Liam would be safe in our apartment.

But it was too small,
stifling
taboo.
Mom's schedule could have changed.

My sisters could come back.

But Liam would be safe.

We could go up to the apartment.
Dahlia should be in bed.

Liam looked toward the teenagers,
this time full face, bolder.
Listening a moment to the racket
of young men, totally absorbed in themselves
and in the passions of their argument.
He frowned, considering.
No, I think you're right. Maybe I should get home.

I tried not to feel rejected.
I tried to feel relieved.

SEPARATE, NOT EQUAL

Mom said she knew when they proposed
the park—
a public park
right next to
their almost finished school—
it was a concession.
They would share it with us.

They'll keep it up that way, at least.

And they did.
Better than the
roofs and books
and pest control
and everything else in our building
and at our schools.

Our bedrooms looked out over the park.
When we were home
we watched the Brookside Hotshots because
we didn't have cable channels
or access to the internet.
Mom said she couldn't trust
the world spilling into us
all day long
everyday
unsupervised.

We all watched the students across the street,
wishing we were them;

wondering if the windows only worked one way.

We could have asked Liam.
Do you guys see us from over there?
Hoping there was a chance they did
and one day they'd let us in.
But there are some questions even Freesia won't ask.

Right before the new school opened,
when we had only been living in Brooks Street Housing
for a few weeks,
a representative held a meeting in our community center.
There will be scholarships,
she said.
Everyone can enter a lottery,
she claimed.
Parents put their children's names in that evening,
filled out a bunch of complicated paperwork,
and attached a copy of their latest report cards,
as requested.
I thought the lottery was supposed to be random?
Freesia sneered.
Mom ignored her.

Most parents knew it was a waste of time.
We'd still have to buy the uniforms,
the books
a meal plan

a laptop
a bunch of things
we couldn't afford.
And even if we could,
we still wouldn't fit in
without fancy cars and overpriced shoes.

Mom didn't care.
She said if any of us got in,
there was no doubt about it.
A way would be made.

Nothing ever came of it.
They prolly used our applications as toilet paper for the custodians,
Freesia said.
And Mom whispered,
Probably.

In my head, Daddy shouted,
Enunciate! And…
(softer)
Don't be so dramatic and crass.
I don't think anyone heard either
of them but me.

No one who lived in Brooks Street Housing
attended Brookside Academy.

INTRODUCTION

We met Liam on a sad Saturday,
in the days surrounding
one year after Daddy was gone.
He'd walked right over to Freesia
and me
while we sat on the park bench closest to our side of the
park.

There aren't really sides,
I told Freesia.

Then how come there are three benches over there
and only one over here?
That's sides.

I knew she was right.
Four divided by two is two.
Two on our side would have been fair.
Don't use that word!
Daddy's voice.
So I ignore Freesia.
If we flip out every time we see small inequalities,
we won't have the energy
to fight for the big ones.

We were reading the day we met Liam
and not watching the Littles
as they swung

slid
merry-go-rounded
seesawed
climbed
hid and ran.

I had learned to hear them without sight.
Every so often I'd take a
a semi-conscious roll call
of their
squeals and giggles
backwards from youngest to oldest.
Dahlia, Amaryllis, Azalea, Zinnia—
Doll, Amie, Zale, Zin.

Mind if I sit?
He'd startled us.
I looked up, squinting into his lush green eyes
fitting like storybook prose into that early spring day.
My periphery revealed
that Freesia'd had the good sense
to use her left hand as an awning
when she looked up.
Her face was a meticulously ironed mask,
unyielding against the sun,
the complete opposite
of my crimped features.
Typical.

I felt like she could
see all of him;

29

take him in
protected.
I never had a chance.

Don't you see all those benches
over there?
She used her right hand to point,
her head following it,
cocked to the side.
Her entire body aimed
at the three empty benches on their side of the park.
No one from Brookside Academy came here on
weekends
except Liam.

I do see them.
He steadied himself then
and gave an irresistible grin.
But I'm not the kind of guy that chooses loneliness
over loveliness.
Freesia groaned
and returned her attention to her book.
Obviously his grin worked only on me.
I scooted to the right
because I knew Freesia wouldn't
make room
for him.

I'm Liam.
He tried to look each of us in the eye
but Freesia wouldn't lift hers

30

from her book.
He took my invitation,
sat down between us,
lifted his right foot assuredly,
placed his right ankle
on his left knee.
He leaned back,
lifted both arms,
and laid them behind us
across the top of the bench.

It was the first time Liam gave me goosebumps.
It reminded me of Daddy
in the car
driving all of us.
He'd put his arm up behind Mom's
head rest,
and I knew
he had our backs.
He would protect us forever.

But Freesia snapped
me back into reality.
She gave me a
Do you believe this guy?
look
and before I could say anything
to at least try to stop her,
You planning to take up this whole bench,
White Boy?
I mean, it's predictable.

31

You, over here acting like you own the place,
but that doesn't mean it's not irritating.

Liam smiled at this.
I'm just trying to make friends.
He winked my way.
I smiled back, shyly.

But Freesia countered,
Well, that might be how you make friends
where you live,
but here we don't colonize.
We assimilate.

He didn't respond,
didn't really move.
But I felt his body shrink
gradually,
infinitesimally,
and his breath flatten.
His chest no longer puffed out
like that bright red flap under a lizard's chin.

It occurred to me that maybe
for the first time
he was aware
of the space he was taking up,
of the oxygen he helped himself to,
and the carbon dioxide
with which he displaced our air.

I'm Iris Hampton.
First and last name
like Daddy taught us.

I threw myself into shifting the climate
surrounding that bench,
determined to blow
Freesia's hostility,
Liam's abasement,

and my simmering, irrepressible captivation
for Liam to the other side of the park.

And, this is my sis…
With one tiny shift in Freesia's posture,
I knew not to continue.

Nice to meet you both.
His words carried less air,
but the slight nod of his head
was steadfast.

That was the beginning
of Freesia's mission
to school Liam
and
the beginning of Liam
changing our minds
about the kids that went to school across the street.

Our public

school schedule
was slightly different from their private
school schedule.
So, on the days we were off and they were not,
we peeked out our windows at the lower grades
as they marched to the park
for recess —
orderly
taking turns,
one at a time —
and back in again to their world of heaps and loads.

They laughed just like us
and teased and argued.
They jumped and swung and climbed.

They really are just like you.

I don't tell anyone I hear Daddy's voice
when I'm at my lowest.
When I feel brave enough to not be here anymore,
Daddy's voice is disappointed in me.
And his discontent is the only thing that keeps me
brave enough to stay.

There's nothing noble about giving up.

I stay.
Living in an apartment
in a section of the city
that used to be only for poor people.

Before we had to move, my sisters and me
had never been to this part of town.
Is it possible that one day
we won't even be able to afford this?
They'll raise the rent,
says Mom,
and throw us out of here,
tear the whole building down
and build a place the Brookside students won't have to ignore.

For now, we live right across the street.

Rich people built a school for their children
on a plot
where low income housing older than ours
was demolished.
I bet they had never been here before either.

How is it that our lives got flipped belly up?
And just across the street we have to look at
what our lives would have been
if Daddy had won the lottery instead of leaving.

Can't win what you don't play.

THE GARDEN

The Flower Sisters
is what Daddy called us:
You were born exquisite!
He said everything from my teeny toes to my
baby's breath
smelled of his mother's garden,
reminded him of his childhood,
made him cry laughing.

Iris.

There's nothing quite like the first baby.
You can never duplicate the awe —
even if you've seen a hundred babies before
YOUR first,
even if you have a hundred after
your FIRST.

Velveteen skin.
In sleep, I draped willowy and feminine
like the petals of the flower
I was named after.

I worried that you had no bones.

It was I who convinced him
that he and Mom could conceive only
blossoms.

36

We almost changed our last name legally.

Mom would smack his arm then, and he'd laugh
a laugh that budded sunlight.
She looked at him like he'd invented flowers.
She convinced us he'd invented happiness.

After me, Daddy planted a garden,
and the more blossoms they conceived,
the bigger the garden grew.

Iris, Freesia, Zinnia, Azalea, Amaryllis, Dahlia.

Mom said they'd prayed for three,
but God
had blessed them two-fold
and granted her The Littles.
He gives us what we need,
Ma Moore says.

At home, we shared rooms in pairs and
still had one to spare.

At home,
Daddy worked all day.
Mom stayed home with us.

We had a yard and a dog and piano.

Then Daddy was gone.

We left the house,
the dog was adopted,
and the piano stayed behind.

It was the garden that everyone wept over.
It was the garden that we all knelt in
and yanked at in fistfuls
until the knees of our pants
and shirt sleeves were stained
with damp earth
and our arms were full of desperately plucked flowers.
We couldn't hold them all.
We couldn't pick them all.
Daddy's garden was
layered,
perennial,
seasonal.
I'd crossed my heart that I would burn it
so no one else could have Daddy's
blossomed brood.
But I couldn't pour the gasoline
I could not ignite the match.

I wondered if Mom still felt like her blessings had
multiplied.
I wondered if someone had revived Daddy's garden.
I hoped they had.
I hoped they hadn't.

In the apartment,
we shared two rooms

configured variably—
three and three,
four and two,
one and five.
Mom lobbed
from pillar to post,
not truly committed to living with us.
Not brave enough to not.
Too brave not to.

We left and came back home
and both ways we saw it—
the school we were not fortunate enough to attend.

One day I screamed it wasn't fair.
We weren't allowed to say that word
when Daddy was alive.

Fair? Is it fair that you throw your Mom's good cooking away
when so many babies in this world
in this country
in the state
in our city
die
because they are hungry?
Life is not fair.
It never will be fair!

One day I said,
Why do they always try to keep Black people down?
Will racism ever end?

I was confident I'd have an ally in Freesia.
Instead she took my head between her hands
stared into my eyes;
her naturally narrow eyes
became slits.

Think about it!
She admonished.
Those students aren't just white.

And she's right.
Some of them are white,
most of them.
But they have coffee colored skin, too—
every kind of coffee.
Some wear scarves or turbans
to cover their hair.
One boy is in a wheelchair.

Her disappointment in me was
demoralizing.
It's not our skin keeping us out.
It's our bank account.
And not because we're poor
but because we're not rich.

Daddy always told us
like it was.
Even if I had stayed,
you wouldn't be going to that school.

If we got in on scholarship,
would we care why other children didn't?

Before Liam,
we focused on those children
with birthright
like changeling hopefuls.
Thoughts of being eligible
preoccupied our existences.

We saw a tormenting incongruity
in life

across the street.

At the apartment,
Mom got up hours before we did.
Exercised.
Showered.
Ate silently.

She didn't kiss us before she left
or when she got home
after we had already gone to bed.

Her hugs were
robotic,
programmed properly,
short-circuiting
just on the cusp of emotion.

41

Freesia was a nest of red ants
constantly
disturbed.
She said Mom hugged us,
listened to us, talked to us
like she'd rather do anything else
than
hug us
listen to us
talk to us.

But I knew Mom wasn't withholding from us.

83% of her was keeping us housed and fed and clothed
10% willing herself to breathe
6% for sanity
6% for when something else went wrong.

She was already in arrears.

The mothers across the street,
if they got out of their fancy cars,
if chauffeurs weren't dropping their kids off,
often took a moment to look back
over their shoulders
through us
like a moment of silent prayer—
gratitude, pity, fear.
Maybe wishing that soon they
wouldn't have to look through us

or be reminded that we existed
at all.
Maybe they'd been promised
eventually we'd be driven out?
I wished they'd turn into pillars of salt.
I wondered which one of them was Liam's mom.

Freesia said they were all doped up
on antidepressants because they felt so sad
about not having any reason to be sad.
She'd glide around the apartment,
phony half-smirk sketched on her face.
They can't smile too big or they'll wrinkle.
They pop pain pills because they had surgery done to their
noses—Freesia wriggled hers
lips—an exaggerated pout
cheeks—she sucked hers in
foreheads—her eyebrows danced one at a time
boobs—she shimmied her chest
butts—she turned, bent, and slapped her own
stomachs—Freesia lifted her shirt to reveal her inverted
belly and outie belly button.

By then, the Littles were puddles of hysterical tears on the
floor.

Surgery so painful they had to keep taking the pills,
and now they can't stop.
She imitates scarfing down handfuls of pills.

I didn't know where she got it.

Freesia told us stories at dinner
that could make pre-ghost Ebenezer Scrooge
giggle like Dahlia,
high-pitched,
jackhammering and snorting.

But Freesia didn't laugh
and her sketched smiles
never personalized.
To Freesia
the people across the street
were a goal to attain.
She had this idea that there was a limited
amount of money in the world,
and they amassed most of it,
and that's why we had so little.
She vowed one day, she would have a lot of money
which meant some of them wouldn't.

It's the same way she felt about Mom
and love;
that it was limited
and went somewhere else.

But I knew Mom's love had nowhere else to go.
If she could have shown her love, she would have.

SABBATH

Every Sunday
without Mom
we Flower Sisters walked
to the church down the street
and to Ma Moore—
who wore *EAU DE LOVE*
and hugged us
heart to heart
and never truly let go.
Still hasn't let go.
She kissed all twelve of our cheeks and our six foreheads.
I knew I was her favorite
even though my sisters all seemed to think the same
about themselves.

Ma Moore is the reason I know
that even though there's a limited amount of money
in the world,
love is the infinity loop.

Ma Moore walked right up to us one day
when we were shopping for school supplies.
We had just moved to Brooks Street.
She smiled at Mom,
and Mom smiled back
with her whole face.
Mom, who sometimes couldn't make herself smile at us.

Daddy would have called Ma Moore a wonder.

Daddy's List of Wonders:

Mom
we Flower Sisters
his mama
his garden
sunsets
jazz
grilled lamb

I don't know where he would have put God—
if he would have put Him anywhere.

We never got to meet his mama because she died when
he was only thirteen,
which is how old I was when Daddy went away.
Ma Moore's smile brought to mind the pictures of
Daddy's mama;
one whiff of Ma Moore let me inhale Daddy's
flashbacks—
his mama and her garden.

Some people smile and it lights them up.
Ma Moore's smile lit me up.
It lit Mom up
that day in the store.

She asked Mom if we had a church home
and didn't wait for an answer.

I think back then you could just look at Mom
and tell she didn't know God.

Mom half-listened, her head nodding on robot pilot
while Ma Moore touted Grace Walk A.M.E.
Ma Moore's conclusion,
Ya'll come sit with me on Sunday, now.
Hear?
dragged Mom back to us.

Her obligatory,
Yes, Ma'am,
a byproduct of embarrassment
for her lack of attention
and Ma Moore's boss demeanor.

From then on,
Mom insisted we spend Sundays there
even though she never set foot inside.
We knew she and Ma Moore
kept in touch sporadically,
so there was no way to fake attendance.

We passed Grace Walk A.M.E.
to get to school and also to Spriggs Park.
It sits back from the road.
You can miss it if you're not paying attention,
but once you see it that first time,
you look for it every time after that.

I could have done without going.

I didn't want to go the first time.
None of us did.
But after that first service,
I looked for Sunday
all through the week.

Grace Walk
is made of thick, dark red brick
the same color
as Jesus' blood
(according to Dahlia).
A huge wooden cross rises from the roof,
so rugged and weathered
Dahlia exclaimed,
Jesus prolly got a million splinters!
Her sentiment was so profound
I didn't bother to correct her English.
The church is huge.
Inside
the walls are wooden,
warm, and damp.
Light from outside
penetrates, filtered
by stained glass Bible scenes
in bright purple, red, blue, yellow, and green.
The sanctuary takes up the entire main floor.
Wall-to-wall pews could fit four hundred people
(Freesia's estimate).
It was only ever full on Christmas and Easter.
Up at the pulpit
on the far left is the baptismal pool.

Dead center is the pastor's podium
with choir risers to the right.

Upstairs are the classrooms for Sunday school,
which I had to teach every other Sunday—
preschool
because it was the only age group
I didn't have younger siblings in.
On my Sundays off, I got to sit
in Adult Sunday school with the other teens.
The church service immediately follows
Sunday school.
In the basement are the kitchen,
dining hall,
and two of the five bathrooms.

If there was a special event,
we spent the entire morning and afternoon in church.
Some Sundays we got home after five,
carrying plates piled high with leftovers,
compensation for the dinners Mom had stopped cooking
since she'd been buried alive.

Grace Walk was the home away from home
the apartment could never be.

Ma Moore called us her *grandbabies*,
and even when her real grandbabies visited,
she kept us close, too.
We learned that Jesus is everything.
We had peers who loved Jesus

and adults who looked after us.
We had Ma Moore,
who wore two anklets on her left ankle
and one on her right,
all three brimming
with bells and charms
given to her as gifts.

Freesia gave her a small rose charm
she'd found under the bus stop bench,
cleaned with toothpaste in the bathrooms sink,
and wrapped in shimmery silver tissue paper.
Free wrote all our names
in a dollar store card
in her best imitation
of my perfect cursive
and let Dahlia present the gift to Ma Moore.

Ma Moore hugged us all,
but she was no fool.
She kissed Freesia's forehead with a
Thank you, Beloved.

Ma Moore's every stride was an undersong.

As soon as we met her
I knew she was the reason God made grandmas
and that He makes up for letting things go
by giving us surprises
we wouldn't encounter without the taken things
gone.

We had no grandparents
and only one half of a parent left.
Until we met Ma Moore buying school supplies.

Once we got our life back together,
and were all married with kids,
Mom would be the Ma Moore kind of grandma.

Until then,
Mom had to pay bills and make sure we had food and
clothes.
She had to wake up early and go to bed way too late,
working and studying.
She had to rely on us Flowers to
cook
clean
get to school on time
do homework
study for tests
make it to church
get along.

She had to live without Daddy,
a flower without sunlight
trying to grow in deserted,
rocky soil,
and hoping for the windswept
mist from rain
that only hydrates the other side of the street.

INTEGRATION

Life spat storms
of cinder blocks
that first summer
we lived in Brooks Street Housing,
the summer it only rained
on the other side of the street.

That summer,
Robby Bolton was murdered.
Shot seven times
in front of his mother
outside the package store on Glenwood Street.
Robby lived four doors down from us.
Fifth floor, Unit F.
The talk in the complex
was that Robby had it coming—
he was in a gang
and he sold drugs—
and that his mother
Should have spent time raisin' Robby
instead of having babies
with every man she met.

Robby Bolton had the kind of smile
that summoned magic.
He was the first person who smiled at me
the day we moved into Brooks Street Housing.
His chalk white teeth

were successive welcome mats
across a face that reminded me of midnight—
warm and shadowy.
He had the darkest skin I'd ever seen.
Skin so lovely that I wished I had it,
jealously considered that it was the kind of characteristic
that was wasted on a boy,
like mile-long eyelashes.
He winked at us from the alley
he usually loitered in.
He always gave Dahlia a strawberry lollipop
and called her, "Little Strawberry."

I didn't understand how anyone could believe
Robby deserved to be shot.
Dropping out of school,
joining a gang,
selling drugs—
All terrible things.

But so terrible that he deserved to die?

In front of his mother?

Robby Bolton's mother had seven children.
Robby was her first,
the only boy.
If she had all those kids,
all those men,
she had to have a lot of love in her.
Most people would never see

someone they loved die.
But I had.

I figured anyone who could say Robby deserved it
and anyone who didn't feel sorry for his mother
had to have a pebble for a heart
and an impaired temporal lobe.

I thought if Robby Bolton
could get killed so close to where we lived
maybe one of us would accidentally get killed too.
Freesia said our building
was the safest one in Brooks Street Housing.
It helps that the Academy is right across the street.

Once we started school,
and Mom started going, too,
she sat
Freesia and me
down on the couch
and knelt in front of us,
her hands spread across our knees.
Grey eyes clasped ours.
It took us straight back home.
This was one of the old ways;
when she had something to say
and needed us to hear every single word.

It was how she gave us the all-about-your-body talk
when I was ten and Freesia nine
and then the sex talk

54

when I was eleven and Freesia ten.
Both those conversations had terrified me
but intrigued Freesia.

It was how she'd announced each of our sisters'
conceptions.

How she told us first,
Daddy's gone.

How we'd found out we had to leave home.

Listen, my beauties,
I'm going to be away a lot
working two jobs.
going back to school at night.
I need the two of you
to keep all of you
safe.

Stay together.
Don't trust anyone who tries to separate you.
There are men out there
who want to do nasty things to little girls,
young women.
Watch your sisters.
Watch yourselves.
Stay together.
No one comes into our apartment,
especially men
but not even boys.

The only house you are ever allowed in
is Ma Moore's,
and even then,
stay together.

Do you understand me?

We both nodded
and just as quickly
as we'd time traveled home,
we were back in the apartment.

That night after Zinnia fell asleep,
I climbed into Freesia's bed,
and Freesia said,
She's so afriad.
And I asked, *Of something specific?*
Something—Freesia grasped my hand—*really bad.*
Someone taking something from us
we'll never get back,
and putting something inside us
that can never be taken out.
Ever.
My entire body clenched as she said the word,
Rape.

Did this happen to you, Free?
I peeled my eyes open.
She kept hers shut,
as if that would protect her.

It happened to Aubrey last summer.
And then, even less than a whisper.
Her uncle.

Tears fought their way through her closed eyes
and skated her flawless cheeks.

Mom had described sex
as something beautiful and
desirable that happened
between a husband and wife.
I had never imagined it could be something
stolen
forced
by someone you knew
and trusted
and loved.

How could Mom bring us
to this awful place
where kids got shot
and raped?
And adults either did it,
or thought they deserved it?

Freesia rubbed my back
as she wiped her tears
then mine,
mixing them.
We have each other.

I wanted to whisper,
And God.
But didn't God love Robbie?
And Aubrey?

Ma Moore once said
God grants sunlight to both good and evil,
And storms assail the just and unjust.

It was like Daddy said,
Life is not fair.
But Daddy agreed with Freesia.
You will always have each other.

To share the sunlight
and shelter one another from the storms.
To shade each other from harsh rays
and to be refreshed together.

We had Liam, too,
But we couldn't tell Mom.
And Daddy was silent on the subject.

WINDFALL

Liam dropped down on our lives
and spread
himself like a canopy.

I had to give myself continuous
conscious reminders
that Liam wasn't God.
Maybe he'd been sent by God,
but he was not our Savior.

I didn't mention this to my sisters.
I wrote *M & S* in tiny letters in the margins
of my notebooks
obsessively
mindlessly,
using the last letters of our names,
just in case they ever noticed.

Liam taught Dahlia to swim in two days,
exactly the way Daddy had taught the rest of us,
a flash flood of confident instructions
sweeping away any doubt.
Dahlia didn't whine once.

He was still a stranger to us then,
this white boy with a
relentless desire
to be with us.

Was it a test from Mom?
Was she standing just outside our sights,
with hands on her hips,
tapping her right foot in irritation?

Daddy made us watch a kidnapping special
on television once.
The parents stood back and watched their kids,
distracted by promises of candy
and sympathy for lost dogs,
forget everything they'd been taught about Stranger
Danger.
*Trustworthy adults never ask children for help. Remember
that!*
Daddy had warned.
And, there was Mom, relying on us.
Stay together
Trust no one.
The world is dangerous.

Liam's persistence
should have been unnerving.
We should have been suspicious.

Instead, we were
enthralled.
Soaked him up
like solar panels.
He illuminated our lives
days after he was gone.
We wanted to be him

or we loved him.
We all saw Daddy in him.

Freesia alone recognized
he needed fixing.

That white boy is like a life raft
with a hole in it.
None of us knew
she was absolutely right.

For those two days
of swim lessons,
I stood by,
ready to jump in,
ready to save Dahlia,
all the while suspecting I wouldn't have to.
After that,
when she doggy paddled all the way across the pool,
smiling snaggletoothed,
Liam had free reign of us.

Liam's entrance into our lives
coincided

with Ma Moore's adopting us,
with our introduction to Jesus,
and a new quantity of life,

with the idea that everything happened
according to a plan

set out by God.

Because it was either God
or despair,
I grabbed His hand,
How do you do?
and welcomed Him into my heart
recklessly.
I trusted Liam in exactly the same way, beyond reason,
without reservation

I believed.

Freesia did not.
Despair filled her dance card.
She let it twirl her, dip her,
spin her around,
lead her.
It swayed her thoughts.
It directed her mood.

It convinced her to resent Liam's privilege.
It wanted her to hate him,
to put him in his place.
Her ego took pleasure in all the ways
he served us,
turning the tables on class.

WELL READ

Every summer since I was five,
Daddy created a reading list
that was passed down to each of my sisters
in turn, so long as he lived.
Somewhere during our move,
the lists were lost.
Like so many other things of Daddy,
of all of us.

Liam came to Spriggs Park one day,
wielding a book about three sisters—
brown like us,
sassy
and bold.

He handed it casually to Amaryllis.
It had been on Daddy's list for the summer after third
grade.

Even that book didn't divorce Freesia from suspicion.

She rolled her eyes as mine filled with tears.
Before you see this as some kind of sign, Iris,
please remember that Amie is only going into third.

O, ye of little faith,
I'd remembered our pastor quoting one Sunday.
I prayed for her.

Open Free's eyes like you did Elisha's. Please!

I didn't answer her there in the park
I knew it would lead to raised voices.
She didn't care what Liam heard,
but I did.
Every time she pushed against him,
I prayed it wouldn't be the last time we saw him.

Free,
I begged her that night.
He's a white boy
who just gave our sister
a book about Black sisters in the summer,
a book on Daddy's summer reading list.
Think about it.
How could he have known?

He's trying too hard,
Iris.
He obviously searched
'great books for tween Black girls.'
Don't be so naive. He wants something.

Even then I doubted
we had anything Liam could possibly want.
But, what? Why would he do all this?
We don't have anything to give.

Not according to Mom.
He could be some sicko.

He's trying to get us to trust him.
Let our guards down.
What he wants?
Don't ask me.
Ask him!

But, then we should stay away from him.

She didn't answer this.
And it took me more than a year
to realize why.

Freesia and I tried our best to recreate
the book lists for the others,
but because I'm the oldest,
I didn't have any more book lists
from Daddy.

I considered it a blessing
and resolved to read every book
of the Bible instead.
Maybe God wanted me to spend more time
getting to know Him.

The next time we went to the library,
Freesia pounded
'great books for Black teens,'
into the search engine,
forcing me to notice
her wry smile.

The day after she brought
a book with a Black girl heroine to the park,
Liam brought one with a Black male protagonist.
She pretended not to notice,
but I read the back cover
and asked him if I could borrow it
when he finished.

It gave us something easy
to talk about.
He understood more than we thought he did
about race issues,
which seemed to annoy Freesia more
than if he hadn't known anything at all.

Maybe Liam could help me with a book list.
I fantasized about having our own private
book club,
but I'd never be able to ditch Freesia
while also keeping her close.

BILINGUAL

There are benefits to economic downfall:
the buoyancy of walking
through corridors
unfamiliar
and feeling familial.
Feet afloat for milliseconds at a time
between sure steps
on equal ground.
Hallways slightly indented,
contoured specifically for us
like memory foam.

Freesia said it was because
I was finally in high school.
I had more freedom.

I looked at her sideways, but didn't say a word.
She had the superior knowledge all preteens
have of a place before they get there.

Freedom is feeling like you can talk
and important people will listen.
It's no one owning the trips you take
or how you get there.
Freedom was before.

Freesia believed that our move
perpetuated a myth.

We were suddenly exactly what
people thought we should be.

But also,
we drifted
without the envy
of hair that billowed and swung
or twirled in ribbons
around dreamy fingers.
We didn't have to wonder why our teachers
weren't calling on us as much as them
or whether they believed the other girl's word against
ours because she reminded them of their daughters or
nieces
or themselves
and we did not.

The new school was a world where the warm smile of the
assistant principal
wasn't five degrees cooler than the one radiated toward
the kid two steps ahead of you
with skin five shades lighter than yours.

At the new school,
we all got that lukewarm smirk
from some.
All of our words had equal veracity
or none at all.
We were all called on.
There was no white option.

Our hair wasn't outnumbered there,
but even if it was,
who had time
to worry about things like hair?

Everywhere
braids defied gravity,
even more magical than Dahlia
suspended
on a seesaw.
Poofs pom-pommed uninhibited
like clouds through the paint-chipped hallways.
Bone straight tendrils swayed
like hips
too big for their own britches.

Here we saw the infinite possibilities
for our hair
and wondered how we ever believed it inferior.

It's not that we weren't ever looked at differently
or treated differently
at our new schools
in our new neighborhood
at the new library
at the new stores.
It was that everywhere we looked
people looked just like
us.
We got to bear the burden of being second class
as a unit,

our yokes were lighter
and our resilience
no longer stood segregated.

We had two distinct hairstyles then,
for school.
The eldest three—
Zinnia, Freesia, and I—
each wore one long silky braid descending our backs
because Freesia had researched Nefertiti
and was convinced
that under her famous cap-crown
a long braid spiraled on top of her head.
The Littles—
Azalea, Amie and Dahlia—
each got one thick cornrow
across each side of her head,
swooping back and down.
Freesia likes to distinguish herself from them,
and the hairstyles were easy to do,
lasted five days,
and they could brush it themselves
each morning.

The hair,
like the laundry and cooking and cleaning and
homework,
spilled on Freesia and me
and singed.
We could both do the intricate styles
that Mom did and Daddy raved over,

70

which lasted ten days,
seven if we swam.
But there was the laundry and cooking and cleaning and
the homework.

We only got fancy for picture day
and church celebrations.
I'd wash, condition, blowout, and trim dead ends.
Freesia braided or styled in buns or ponytails.
An understaffed assembly line.
We tried to teach Zinnia,
but she wasn't interested.

Back at school
The teachers fell into two categories;
they pitied us
or they saw
us in all of our glory.

We no longer had to compete with anyone
in ways we couldn't control,
but we still couldn't control everything about how we
were seen.

Is there harm in trying?
I could still hear Daddy.
Don't let stereotypes define you;
be unpredictable.

Daddy used to say that we are all
placed into categories

by people who look at us
and make assumptions
and we reciprocate that labeling
with everyone we see,
every one of us victim and perpetrator.
The challenge is to ignore the story
you're telling yourself
and allow the individual
to tell you who she really is.

One day at the public pool
as we lay out on our favorite lounge chairs
arranged the way we were always arranged —
Freesia, Liam, me —
Liam whispered
Do you think race is an illusion?

Huh? Freesia, only half awake.

Like, does our race determine
who we are?
Or are we who we are
because of what other people
think we are
when they see us?

I almost got lost in thoughts of Daddy,
but I brushed them away;
focused on the Father.

God makes us who we are,

and it has nothing to do with race.
The world tries to define us.
Satan tries to destroy us.
We are who God says we are.

But Freesia:
Race is an illusion.
Some of us are predefined by the world.
We don't control what the world says about us,
and even when we try to change their minds,
we can't.
Their minds are set.

And Liam:
How do we figure out who God wants us to be?

And me:
You have to have a relationship with Him.
Pray and read the Bible.
You should come to church with us.

Iris, he can't!
Freesia bolted upright,
no longer half asleep.
Ma Moore might tell Mom.

So you DO like hanging out with me?
Liam's smile should be on magazine covers.

Don't flatter yourself, White Boy.
You're a free babysitter for the Littles.

73

Freesia turned her back to us then.
I closed my eyes.
I heard Liam turn to face me,
but I kept my face pointed toward the sky
and my eyes closed.

Iris, is there really a God
up there who loves us?

Yes.

Then why would He
let someone as boss as you
lose everything
and someone spoon-fed
and selfish like me
have everything?
Wouldn't He make it so you have the better life?

Ma Moore says we all get rained on
and we all get sunlight.
I didn't know Him.
I didn't find Him
until Daddy left
and we had to move.
He made something really good
come out of something really awful.

We met you.
I wanted to say, but didn't.

74

I should have said,
And you're not selfish or spoon-fed…
Well, maybe spoon-fed.
But you work hard.
You're generous and sympathetic.
You are ace, Liam.

Instead I whispered,
But Freesia hasn't found Him.

Because she hadn't submitted.
But I believed she would
because it was my fervent prayer.

He's all powerful, right?
So He could make people come to him
by just saying to them, loudly and undeniably,
'I'm here for you. I love you. Come here.'
He could make good things happen and take credit for them.
He could stop our suffering.
He could have kept Eden perfect.

He doesn't make us do anything, Liam.
He doesn't want robots.
We have free will so we can choose.
He loves us that much.

But, Iris, our parents don't love us that way.
They tell us we have to
get good grades;

play on teams we hate;
play instruments we despise;
learn different languages, hoping they'll benefit us down the
road.

They tell us it's our job
to make a difference,
to impact the world,
to be even better than they are.
They tell us where to go,
to eat more vegetables,
drink only water,
respect authority
but also question authority.
They justify all of it with 'love.'

Our parents are only human.
Human love is imperfect,
demanding,
God's love is freeing.
Parents can change our actions.
God changes hearts.

I don't know,
He was unsettled.
Sounds like a cop-out.
Sounds neglectful and apathetic.

I didn't tell him it was
my relationship with God
that made me different from him and Freesia—

76

content and secure.
I didn't know if I could
without sounding superior.
Ma Moore said the worst
thing we can do when trying to disciple
is to be self-righteous.
I wasn't any better
than Freesia and Liam.
But deep down, I felt I was.

The two of them were always
unstable
searching
longing
desperate.
I talked myself into contentment 99% of the time.
I reminded myself that joy was a minute-by-minute
choice.

When we first moved to Brooks Street Housing,
Everyone wanted to know about us.
Kids asked the questions
adults wanted answered.

It's a funny thing when you stand out
not for how you look
but for being unknown.

There was a community
made up of people connected
in a web of past experience.

They knew
Miss Viola always needed a loan,
and she could be trusted to pay it back.
Deandra Swat couldn't even be trusted
to pay you back two eggs.
But Donte McKnight would always
lend them to her
or anything he had
to anyone
without expecting anything in return.

We learned a little
here and there,
but mostly we walked
toward friends and enemies alike
with blindfolds on.

We belonged
back in our neighborhood, our house, with Daddy
for all the reasons Liam found restraining,
for reasons that don't matter as much when you're trying
to survive:
stellar grades
learning a foreign language
playing instruments
a mom and a dad
there with you every day,
inspiring you to change the world.

These things matter when you have the luxury
of reaching beyond survival.

We belonged
at Brooks Street Housing
for reasons that make all the difference in the world:
color
income
status

Mom told us we better not tell
anyone
anything.

Where they come from?
They all got the same Daddy?
Where they Daddy at?
Why she don't ever speak to no one?
Why they got to talk all uppity… so white?
They think they better than us!

Like whiteness and blackness are ways of talking.
Like whiteness and blackness are constraints anyone
should accept.

Mom would kill us if we ever spoke improperly.
Because she thinks we're better than them?
No.
Because life is hard enough as a brown girl.
Because we can't afford to be anything but exceptional.

We had a kid come to our old school.
Arad had the most beautiful eyelashes—

yards of jet black velvet,
finely sliced.
Totally wasted on a boy.

He didn't speak any English.
I wondered what it would be like
to sit in a room full of people speaking a foreign language
expecting me to learn.
I wondered how Arad would ever learn something he
didn't know
just being surrounded by it.

For months
he never spoke.
He never even motioned,
never moved except to follow the rest of us,
a deaf mute.
And then, one day, he broke out
in full sentences—
whispered at first, with doubt—
but soon he confidently
engaged the rest of us
and our teacher.

When did you learn English?
I asked him because I couldn't believe it.

All along.
He shrugged.
*It was like listening to gibberish
and then half-gibberish*

and then I knew it.

Freesia is my favorite sister.
In the old house,
we shared a room,
just us,
and stayed up too late,
whispering about every single
nothing
until I'd fall asleep to the sound of her mumbles.

We had laugh attacks so severe
we honest to goodness
couldn't stop.
Breathless,
we believed we would actually die
laughing,
which made our laughter more frantic,
willing to die young
if only like that.

We fought just as hard as we laughed—
over clothes and jewelry and
friends.
Over space and air,
the remote control
and couch cushions.
We spent too much time together
that was never enough.

I cried to Daddy once,

She's so strong!
after a vicious contest of nasty words
that left me butchered
and her without a nick.

Following the duel,
an equally savage cold war
of silence
stalked me,
omnipresent,
knotted my stomach.
Freesia chuckled
with the other Flowers
and chattered with friends on the bus,
while the iron curtain
of her frigidity
crushed my insides.

It was always I who waved
the white flag.
But that time I wouldn't—
couldn't—
my heart too weak to pick through
my own remains
to find the banner
and to lift it toward her.
To forgive.

I'd sobbed in a muddled mess of affliction—
¼ idolatry
¼ jealousy

¼ vexation
⅛ praise
⅛ death wish

She's so strong?
Why do you say that?
Daddy cocked his head,
and for a fraction of a millisecond,
I thought he was teasing me,
and for that fraction, my vexation shifted to rage.
Beyond his tone and the tilt of his head,
his eyes were innocent.
So my claws retracted, gratefully.
You mistake tears for weakness,
Petal.
Your sister is too scared to let you see
she loves you like flowers love bees.
You? You lay your heart out for the world
to do what it must.
That takes courage.
You can be the victor here.
Victory is not prideful;
it is humble and gracious.

The way Daddy talked about love
and relationships
was biblical.
Even if I didn't know it.
Even if he didn't know it.

Back then,

I couldn't comprehend
a world
where Freesia would be
afraid of anything.
Weaker than me.
The underdog.

But then Daddy left
and Freesia didn't cry.
And I remembered what Daddy said.

TO SOFTEN STONE

Ma Moore announced
she would assign
each of us a Bible verse.
She'd given both of her daughters
and all six of her grandchildren Bible verses,
all around the time they turned three years old.
For each of them, she'd prayed for God to lead her.
Three years old is when your loved ones
can pretty much figure out your flesh,
who you are going to be
and would be
without the intervention of God.
I'm a little late getting to know you all.
But God has never failed me yet.
I know He'll lead me to a verse for each of you,
my destined grandchildren.

I can't remember Freesia at three
because I was only one when she was born.
But all my other sisters have been exactly
who they are since three,
just like Ma Moore said.

Azalea got her verse first,
and even Freesia conceded, after that,
that maybe Ma Moore had someone divine
on speed-dial.

Freesia predicted Azalea's verse would be
the one that says
Woe is me—Isaiah 6:5
Azalea complained constantly
about how unfair her life was.
According to her,
every one of us was prettier,
faster,
smarter,
more beloved,
better liked.
Plus, I'm the only one who's chubby!

It's true we all have less patience for Azalea,
but it's because of her constant whining
(even more than Dahlia).
But it's also true that when she forgets herself,
she's hilarious.
One well-timed wisecrack from her
and I snicker
sometimes months later, just thinking about it.

And she did have to work harder
in school,
but she managed straight A's
always, which no one else
except Amaryllis
ever achieved.
The way Azalea used to carry her report cards home
is the way I imagine God looks at us
and holds us up

when we please Him.
We're a heck of a lot of work,
but then when the work pays off,
well, it makes your whole soul smile.

I wished I felt that way about something.

Azalea was such a good judge of character,
even at eleven.
We spent nearly every moment with other adults
without Mom,
and we traveled all over the city together.
We all looked to Azalea to read situations and people.
She was the one without the blindfold.

She would lead us safely.

Freesia didn't read the whole verse,
or she would have known that putting it on Azalea
wasn't a dig.
Isaiah knew he was ruined because he saw the Lord.
He admitted his own fault and the fault of those around
him.
He was just a regular guy who happened to know God.
He was just like the rest of us.
Freesia still didn't get just how much freedom
came with knowing God.

This is how Ma Moore gave out verses—
she took each one aside,
read the entire chapter

in the airy, deep voice she reserved
for Bible reading
and praying.
Then she highlighted the key verses
in purple highlighter.

My M'Dear believed that the Bible was too precious to write in.
We kids weren't even allowed to touch it.
But I want you all to use your Bibles so much
they look tattered by the time you have someone to pass
your wisdom down to.
Write in every inch of space.
Highlight every verse that makes you want to
shout
or laugh
or cry.
Every verse that kneads your soul or
confounds your mind.
Turn pages down.
Study this book better than you study those school books
you got
taped together.

Freesia was wrong;
Woe was her.
Azalea got 1 Peter 2:9.

But you are not like that, for you are a chosen people. You are
royal priests, a holy nation, God's very own possession. As a
result, you can show the goodness of God, for He called you out
of the darkness into His wonderful light.

After Ma Moore explained it to her,
she commanded Azalea to teach it to us
that evening.
So, during our dinner—
homemade
baked macaroni and cheese with steamed broccoli—
Azalea recited her verse
and the interpretation.
We listened because we knew there would be a quiz.
Freesia, by choice
the most Bible insecure of all of us,
took mental notes.
The following Sunday,
Ma Moore sat with us
at one of the dining hall tables
in the basement of the church
and asked who wanted
to explain Azalea's Bible verse.
Amaryllis raised her hand, but Ma Moore reached out
and enfolded it,
kissed the top of it,
and set it on the table
like it was a butterfly's wing.

Under the pressure of her enduring gaze,
Freesia finally caved.

I'll do it because you all are taking too long;
and I have to study for my science test.
She continued, feigning annoyance,

astounding me.
She displayed zero reverence;
not
holding her shoulders up,
inflating her lungs
elongating her neck
altering the tenor and tone
of her voice.
She slouched and mumbled
and rolled her eyes.
It's about how Jesus came to save us
and how some people reject him.
They stumble through life and falter,
but God's people
choose to trust and follow Him,
are kind of owned by Him and also part of a group,
and that means you have to reject the darkness of the world
and reflect the wonderful light of God.

Ma Moore looked at Freesia then
the way Azalea looked at her report cards,
the way Daddy used to look at me.
Ma Moore held Freesia's gaze in hers,
only long enough for her to register the embrace,
not long enough for Freesia to feel constrained.

Ma Moore looked at Azalea
See there, you have been chosen by the Almighty Himself.
You have a responsibility to the light
over the darkness.
Your life will not be stumble free.

But if you love Him,
if you want Him,
you will stumble, always,
into a closer relationship with Him,
with a holy nation of believers
alongside you.

After that, we walked home,
arms full of bags
full of containers
full of food
Ma Moore had cooked for us.

Zinnia got her verse a couple weeks later.
Zinnia was Azalea's rival
by default,
even though Amaryllis is younger and better
in school than both of them,
because no one can compete with Amaryllis.
Azalea launched accusatory arrows at Zinnia
deeming her culpable for all that
was wrong with her life.
They bounced off Zinnia,
her force field of grace
impermeable.
If I wanted some extra chore done,
Zinn would do it even though it wasn't her chore
or wasn't her turn.
She never got caught up in the preteen
girl drama encapsulating
junior high

like the rest of us did
or will.
She had this way of subduing
Azalea and Dahlia
when all Freesia and I had the patience
for was
the monstrous attempt at
breaking them.

None of us were surprised that Proverbs
held Zinnia's verse—
Proverbs 4:23.
Guard your heart above all else, for it determines the course of
your life.

Zinnia is our sage.

Ma Moore says Satan will try to persuade
me toward destruction.
He attacks those who are on a straight path.
My verse tells me to guard my heart
because it will determine my path.
Basically, I must avoid the evil
and focus on my goal of Christ.
My feet will follow my eyes.

Once again, it was Freesia
who had to explain it back to Ma Moore.
That Sunday, we'd gone straight home after church,
and Ma Moore had come later.
We cooked dinner for her.

We hadn't seen her in nearly two weeks
because she'd gone out of town
to one of her daughters
to celebrate her ninetieth birthday.
So we had a belated party
for her on a day that Mom could
come home early enough to sing *Happy Birthday*
and eat cake and ice cream.

Mom was too thin.
Her face sagged into a perpetual frown
her hair in fleece curls, low cut
and mostly silver.

Amaryllis
learned how to walk at nine months,
could run at ten months,
learned how to read when she was not quite three,
could identify and spell a thousand sight words
by the summer before Pre-K.
In November of her kindergarten year,
she won the school-wide spelling bee
and was promptly moved to first grade.
She could always do Azalea's homework, no problem.
We knew she'd have to skip to fifth grade
a quarter of the way through third.

We told her she was a genius,
because she was
and we needed her to hear it from us first.
Plus, telling her made us feel we could all

own a part of it.

Of course Ma Moore gave Amaryllis three key verses
instead of one—
Proverbs 3: 5-7.

*Trust in the Lord with all your heart; do not depend on your
own understanding. Seek His will in all you do, and He will
show you which path to take. Don't be impressed with your own
wisdom. Instead, fear the LORD and turn away from evil.*

I can't get a big head because I'm a genius.
I have to depend on the Lord and not on my own brain.
I should fear the Lord.
Not like, "Be afraid,"
but like, "Be in awe."
Like, "Wow!"

With this her eyes grew large.
She raised her fists
and blasted her fingers out like fireworks.

With how vast his wisdom is,
I have to make sure I'm doing what He wants
and always remember
the "smart" thing
might not be the wise thing.
I have to pray a lot!

Spoiled rotten
Dahlia,

selfish and impulsive,
but her bitter is so sweet
she could charm the purple
off a prince.
She was the family mayor.
She knew everyone in the building
and every piece of gossip from every family,
and she managed to get information even from adults
without divulging anything about us.
At her old school and the new,
she got to know all the teachers
and campaigned each year for her pick,
scheduling private appointments and
making sound enough arguments to the principals
that she always got her choice.

But she's such a storyteller
(we're not allowed to call her a liar)
that we can never figure out when the truth
parked its car
and her imagination
entered the speedway.
Most of the time,
her fictions preoccupy us surreptitiously.
We don't want to know the truth.

Dahlia was so proud when she finally got her Bible verse,
mostly because she didn't get hers last.
From being born to starting school,
getting her hair done to riding rollerblades,
even threadbare clothes went to her last.

James 1:19
Understanding this, my dear brothers and sisters: You must all
be quick to listen, slow to speak, and slow to get angry.

God gave me two ears and
one mouth,
so I have to listen more than I talk,
and I cannot get angry over little things
because it will keep me from being like Jesus.

We started saying
Quick to listen, slow to speak!
whenever we got backtalk from Dahlia,
wrongfully
using her Bible verse against her
in a way that both developed her
and bridled her,
making our lives easier.

Slow to get angry!

I heard Amaryllis whisper to Dahlia once
as she poured the last of Dahlia's favorite cereal into her
bowl.
My conscience wouldn't allow me to chastise
her for twisting God's word to suit herself,
since I resorted to the same
more regularly than I'd care to admit.

In a twist that struck me like a sixteen-wheeler,
96

and then shifted gears to reverse and roll over me again
for good measure,
Freesia's verses came next.
Freesia had this belief that even though I had been born
first,
she was the eldest in every way that mattered.

It was true, she took charge.

The spotless condition of our tiny apartment,
was Freesia's doing.
She was dogmatic in her approach to cleanliness
and orderliness.
She took no prisoners for things out of place,
reasoning that we had no time for things misplaced.
We complied for fear she'd trash our treasures.

If you put it where it belongs, you'll never have to look for it!
She'd shout on the rare occasion
that something was found out of place,
or, even more dangerous,
something was lost.

Freesia spent precious library time
scouring clearance sales at the thrift store next door
for things
like frames,
coordinating but not identical,
to hold current school pictures.
She lined the pictures up
youngest to oldest

(so Dahlia could be first)
above hooks that held our lunch boxes and book bags
neatly by the door,
above a cubby unit that held our two pairs of shoes each,
on top of which Freesia placed three plush seat cushions.
(She bragged for six months about how she got all three
for $1.50.)
The shelves served as a long bench
on which the Littles sat to take off and put on their shoes.

Every inch of our apartment had been put
to its most efficient use
all because Freesia required,
demanded
order.

Freesia will be the one we call
for trendy organization
when we have homes of our own
filled with children
who come home from school
and throw their bookbags on the floor,
kick their shoes off in the middle of the doorway,
and run for the pantry,
starved.

Freesia will pop in for a visit
and install bookshelves and coat hooks
and a corner piece in a
place we'd never contemplated.
She'll organize nurseries and offices,

cupboards and coat closets.

We'll grumble while she's there,
doing things we never asked her to.
Our homes look just fine and she's never satisfied.
Dahlia will be righteous in her happy chaos
and Zinnia in her stark simplicity.
Still, Freesia will assail.

She'll throw away things we'll never miss,
add touches that make us yearn
for her when she's gone.
We'll do everything better afterwards.
Amaryllis will call her and tell her just how
much she appreciates the neatnik
in her.
Azalea will not call her
but she may call me
and tell me, knowing
I'll tell Freesia.

Ma Moore gave Freesia her verses secretly.
I only found them
by accident.

Our seven Bibles always sat on the third shelf of a
bookcase
that came from home.
One of the only pieces we still had.
Next to the Bibles was a picture of Daddy
from his last week with us,

smiling wide enough to swallow the whole world,
posing next to his garden,
hand outstretched trying to get one of us to stand with
him.
None of us remember lucidly that week,
that month
when he died.
Was it me?
Or was I doing homework?
At gymnastics?
Washing dishes?
Hiding inside for fear he'd make me weed with him
if he saw me?
We each envisioned ourselves
as the beckoned daughter.
It could have been any combination
from all of us
to one of us.
All we knew for sure was that Mom
had taken the picture.
If we'd only known beforehand, we'd have committed
everything to memory.

If a Bible were to go missing,
if anything were to go missing,
it would not be Freesia's.
But her Bible was not
on the shelf—
on the third row
next to Daddy's final photo—
when I grabbed mine

to prepare my lesson plan for church.

At first I went looking for it in an attempt
to ward off the knock-down
drag-out
that was guaranteed
if one of the other girls had taken and not returned
Freesia's Bible.
But why would anyone want Freesia's Bible,
hardly used?
The rest of us took pride in our personal Bibles' wears and
tears.
We weighed them against one another with pride,
veterans comparing battle scars.
Every contact was an opportunity to scuff
it up just a bit more.
To make Ma Moore proud.

The price tag sticker remained attached
to Freesia's Bible.
She hadn't even written her name
on the line above
This Bible Belongs To,
"Ma Moore" on the line above
Given to By,
or the date she'd received it.
Most of the time she forgot to take it to church.
As far as I knew, she'd never actually opened it.
She refused to teach Sunday school,
even as a substitute when I was sick.

But then an idea washed over me
and I felt the relief
of answered prayer.
What if Freesia *was* reading her Bible now?
What if she was finally looking for God?
Her Bible became the key to knowing.

The bigger bedroom in our apartment
contained two sets of bunk beds,
where the four youngest girls slept,
and one of the three student desks we owned,
which Amaryllis and Dahlia shared.
In the smaller bedroom
stood a bunk bed for Freesia and me opposite
Mom's twin sized bed
and the second student desk,
which Azalea and Zinnia shared.

The living space, however, in the bedrooms
was not so compartmentalized.
Books, bangles, brushes, bras,
although organized and separated,
didn't necessarily
live in the room their owners
slept in.

I finally
found
Freesia's Bible in the back of the closet
in the room the younger girls shared.
Her verses

(plural)
were written
on a sticky note
affixed diagonally
to the front cover
of her Bible
in Ma Moore's shaky script.

Comfort: Psalm 46:1-3
Wisdom: Proverbs 18:10
Peace: Isaiah 26: 3-4

I read each verse,
my skin slowly pickling
with salty
envy.

Why hadn't Ma Moore given Freesia
verses about hardened hearts
and the wrath of God?
Romans 2:5
Or controlling her tongue?
Psalm 52:2
Why had Freesia gotten three?
And in secret?
She hadn't had to explain them to us!
When would I get my mine?

I threw her Bible against the back wall of the closet.
It landed
with a thud

spread eagle
on the floor
exposing my discovery.
I left the door cracked,
indecisive
longing to hide my snooping
and ever emboldened
to let it be known.

I went back to my Bible lesson;
God spoke to me,
unmistakable as a burning bush.

Of all the stories in the Bible,
that week, I had to teach
Cain and Able.
Jealousy between siblings.
How it destroys families.
How it causes death.
It was always there in me,
a contempt for Freesia
symbiotic
with my love for her.

Also
always with me,
a softening voice from God,
warning me,
assuring me
that the last will come first
and the first last,

that only a few
will be chosen.

Freesia's new obsession is Egypt.
Eighty percent of the books she checks out of the library
(Mom makes us go there twice a week)
are about her beloved civilization.
I think she'd gladly be transported back in time
to live when pharaohs ruled,
even if it meant laboring without rest or pay
to build one of their great pyramid graves.

She's into the science behind all the great
Egyptian structures
and stuck on the theory that the ancients used
certain plants to soften the stones
for building and moving.

I think it's because Daddy's garden had a way of doing
that
for her.

I used to watch them out there,
knowing I wasn't invited.
Daddy's arm would be around her
or they would both be sitting on the ledge,
her feet dangling,
his firmly planted.
Daddy's animated arms blowing
into the breeze of his zest
for life

as he spoke.
Freesia angry
or sad
or confused
but never for very long.
Daddy tenderized
her
in his garden.

We didn't have Daddy anymore.
But, we had God.
Maybe God could use me to tenderize
Freesia
Like Daddy used to.

DEATH IN THREES

We spent three home game
Saturdays in a bougie
part of town,
on a hill overlooking
Clement Culley Futbal Stadium

From there we could listen
to the Littles play
with *friends* they'd just met
behind us
and gaze down the hill
to watch Liam play soccer.

We knew he could play soccer.
He spent hours
with Zinnia and Amaryllis,
the three of them juggling,
sometimes three balls side-by-side-by-side,
sometimes one ball
in a keep-it-up triangle.
He always commanded them delicately.
He would bribe Azalea
to play 2v2 matches with them,
giving her the coveted creamy, white chocolate bars
his mom brought back from her London
business trips.
Liam and the Littles played
World Cup for hours.

Positive attitude everyone,
and try your best
or no one gets ice cream cones.
Now, GO!
He directed them the entire time,
never out of breath,
patience never lost.
We grew accustomed to hearing,
Dribble, dribble, dribble.
Attack!
First touch! It's all in the first touch!
Do NOT be afraid to head this ball. Head!
That's you! That's you. Control it.
Oh my gosh, you just megged me!
That was sick!
He'd send chip passes to Zinnia,
expecting her to
Settle the ball. Control it. First touch!

Two minutes into the first game
in that bougie C.C.F.S.,
Zinnia abandoned our sisters
and her playmates
and sat on the downslope
in front of Freesia and me,
mesmerized.
We were not prepared
for the spectacle
of Liam on a soccer pitch.

Liam had confided

in us that he didn't fit in
with his team,
that *team* wasn't even the right word.
It was a squad of competitors,
jealous of others' successes
with gleeful mocking
in failure of any kind,
fixated only on being individual phenoms.
Daggers disguised as eyes
designated him for defeat
before he even connected his first touch.
(It's all in the first touch!)

Even parents
willed him to be injured.
It's a cutthroat game,
but soccer is my thing.
When I play, I don't have to think.
I just do.

I heard once that hard work matters
more than talent,
especially when talent sits around expecting
to win
without drive.
I worked my butt off to get on this team
two years in a row!
It's the best team
within a one hundred mile radius.
Believe me, my dad did the research!
So I'll just keep dodging daggers.

We didn't have to know anything
at all about soccer
to see Liam was linked to the ball.
His foot told it what to do and it obeyed.
The ball whispered to him alone
where it was headed,
and the two of them met there.
He outran everyone else,
dribbled around them,
chipped the ball over their heads
to himself
and caught it with a magnetic foot
on the other side.
He did this unbelievable backward
windmill thing, and Zinnia cheered.
Bicycle Kick! Did you see that, Amaryllis?
By then, Amaryllis had joined us too.

If I had been on Liam's team,
I might have hurled daggers at him, too.
Whenever someone else got the ball,
his skills were that much clearer.
He could have been the instructor
and they his clumsy pupils.

He's like a soccer god!
Zinnia turned to us awestruck
at halftime.

I snarled.

Never say that again!
We're not supposed to have any idols before God!

I didn't say he came before God.
He's lowercase.
He can come after. But, he's definitely a go…
My face didn't leave room for ambiguity
as apparently my voice had done.
Zinnia winced and finished,
…royalty.
Like a soccer king.

Soccer king is better.
I smiled at her, superior.
She turned away, battered.

I didn't look at Freesia.
I knew she'd stolen daggers
from Liam's teammates
and was hurling them at me.
You're so severe about God.
You'll make us all hate him!
She'd whispered to me one night.

Ma Moore said you can't be anyone's conscience.
God gave everyone free will for a reason.
The best way to reach people is to love them.
God knows what He's doing.
So we follow His lead.

It made me think of Liam's question

about free will
and parents.
Was it more loving to force God on my sisters,
or to simply show them
and hope
they'd catch on?

And if I tried to force them
to see Him as He is,
wouldn't that mean I don't trust Him
to get the job done?

CONGREGATION

I looked forward to Sunday all week long.
We woke up early,
ate breakfast,
got ready for church,
and walked the ten blocks,
rain or snow or hot, blinding shine.
Inside
we split up
and went to our respective
classes for Sunday school.
Twice a month, I taught
the preschool lesson.

When Miss Brown
announced
the upcoming sesquicentennial
for
Grace Walk African Methodist Episcopal Church,
Dahlia whispered
What's ses… quachy… somethin'?
And Freesia answered quietly,
A 150 year birthday,
at the same time I whispered
Shhhhhhhh!
and glared at them both.

Wow!
Dahlia whisper-shouted, ignoring me.

This church is as old as the Jesus cross
and Ma Moore!
Ma Moore chuckled.
Not quite… and it's something, not somethin'!
Conspiratorially, she winked at me.
But I looked away—
I hadn't forgiven her
for Freesia's verses.

The church's birth story
had been passed down for
its whole life.
The founders were
former slaves,
Willie and Elizabeth Woolfolk,
who migrated to the North
shortly after Emancipation.
They purchased a run-down shack
on a small plot of land.
Rumor had it,
the shack had been a station
in the Underground Railroad.
They lived in the shack
and built it up,
and the shack became the church.
Willie was a preacher.
He built his congregation
and the building grew
with the church.

Back then, it wasn't anything
114

but an old broken down building
with a dirt floor.
But our forebearers built it up over time.
Those that knew about architecture,
electricity, plumbing, insulation,
they pooled their resources,
and they turned a shack built on dirt
into a rock solid church.
That's what you girls need to know;
you can start out
with a dirt floor and no roof at all,
but if you all work together toward
the advancement of His kingdom,
you will find yourselves living in
a house built on a rock.
God is that rock!

Our Sundays were
old ladies in bright dresses
and elegant, matching hats
nodding their heads
and sighing, *Um, hm,*
or calling, *Preach it!*
through entire sermons
while men in stiff sharp suits and synchronized ties
stood like the soldiers at every entrance,
passed the collection plate down each row,
and served us communion.
Young moms with babies sat in the back,
at the ends of pews.
When their babies started to fuss,

they could ease up from their seats
and out of the sanctuary
exactly as effortlessly and silently
as the goo
we made in Science
used to slide back and forth
across our hands
before Mom made us throw it all away.
Goo was not allowed in our apartment.
It wasn't allowed inside at home either,
but at home we had a garage.

Mr. Goodall, who is *just a little bit slow,*
lived in a tiny room set up for him
on the third floor
and cared for the church.
Like he cared for his poor mama
before she got carried off to heaven.
Every Saturday night, he bought dozens
of donuts for all us kids to have on Sunday
after service.
We stood in a line,
nodding and salivating,
Smallest to tallest.
And he asked,
Did you behave?
before handing one to each of us.

On nice days, we spent Sunday afternoons
behind the church
at the playground,

116

Freesia and I laid out across metal benches
with school work or a book,
the rest of the girls ripping and running
like chickens with they heads cut off
with other kids their ages.

Freesia and I didn't have cell phones
like all of the other kids our age
to text or chat
or take selfies with filters
that could disguise us
and present us to the world
memorialized as what the world told us
we should look like.
It may have been a hedge of protection.
It forced us to live in the moment.
It helped us find comfort in truth.
It freed our minds to build relationships.
But
at times
it was isolating.

Freesia said we were like a time-traveling family
from 1990.
We didn't get an allowance
or go shopping at the mall,
at least occasionally,
like we used to,
like every other girl we knew.
Our mom didn't order things for us online
that appeared in boxes two days later.

117

Mom bought all the clothes and shoes we'd get
for a season in one trip by herself
and brought the bags home for us to
rummage,
claim,
and trade.
She no longer took our individual tastes into account.
A lot of times we got hand-me-downs
from families at church,
always delivered privately to Ma Moore,
who presented them to us
with solemn guardianship.

We weren't looked down upon,
not excluded.
We felt loved by the adults at church
and liked well enough by the kids.
No nastiness
nor superiority confronted us.

But there was a distinct correlation
between how we connected with our peers
and the years we'd been alive.
The older we were, the less we meshed.
The younger girls had no issue at all.
Zinnia started to feel a pull
toward Freesia and me,
suspended in that time warp,
outcast and stranded,
foreigners

in our own land.

I wished we could bring Liam.
He had become like fertile soil
for us flowers.
A cool, sunny spot for our petals
to unfurl without fear
of stomping feet.

Liam once told us he didn't fit in
at Brookside Academy,
and in the second
it took her to realize he wasn't joking,
Freesia laughed out loud.
Then her laugh was clipped.
They don't get me there.
His ingenuous expression
echoed inside Freesia and me.
We understood not being gotten.

DEATH NUMBER TWO

When Mother Brown died,
we skipped the viewing and funeral
but attended the repass.
Ma Moore meandered earnestly between
Mother Brown's children and grandchildren,
replaying memories,
reheating neglected plates,
and reassuring everyone.
The Good Lord is still in control.

When Mother Brown's sister lamented
that she'd lost her husband
just a few weeks prior
and a friend of hers had died four months earlier,
Ma Moore shook her head.
Death always comes in threes.
Our Father has His ways.

I gagged on the sip of magic juice
I'd just taken.
Ma Moore's delicious mixture
of ½ lemonade and ½ ice tea,
sweetened with agave nectar,
was highly coveted,
but my stomach clenched
and threatened to push back up
both that sip and
the meal I'd gorged on.

I couldn't eat or drink anything else
that day.

For weeks I lay awake at night wondering
who else would die
and when?
I wanted to ask Ma Moore,
How close do they have to be to qualify?
Did Mother Brown count?
What's the time frame exactly?

Weeks later,
I was walking home from school, blithely
alone.

In our district,
high school started and ended first,
then elementary school,
and middle school last.
It worked perfectly for our family.
Mom didn't have to worry about the Littles,
and for thirty glorious minutes I could do anything
I wanted without worrying about anyone else.

I turned the last corner before
our apartment
and slammed smack into
two fire trucks
an ambulance
three police cars and
news vans

in the middle of the street
between the school and our apartment complex.

Yellow tape screamed in black caps lock

—POLICE LINE DO NOT CROSS—

and sectioned off a large area in front of the school
and a smaller area
around the corner.
Parents and students and teachers and residents
filled the sidewalk on our side of the street only.
Sobbing.
Clasping hands and hugging.
Staring.
Murmuring in death tones.

The mood
flashed me back
to when Daddy died.
There had been no news cameras
or yellow tape,
but there had been an ambulance
and police cars
and sobbing,
clasped hands,
hugging.
Murmured death tones
followed us
for months.

I worked my way into the crowd and stood
staring across the street,
pretending to be looking
but not.
Just by listening,
I found out a student had jumped
from the roof.

If that was true,
if a Brookside Academy kid actually fell off that roof,
it had to be a result of a foolish group goofing off
on the roof.
Accidental.
Either that, or some spoiled heir's
cry for help had gone wrong.
There's no way one of them would jump
on purpose.
They all had everything.

Could supreme privilege coexist
with hopelessness?

As the details vibrated around me,
my mind saw Freesia
climbing the stairs,
breaking a lock
(because surely it would have been locked),
sauntering to the edge,
looking down and still finding the strength,
convincing herself that maybe she'd fly,
and stepping over,

123

arms outstretched,
her shirt sleeves alone blowing upward,
trying to reach heaven.

But everyone said the jumper was a *he*.

I ran to our building then
and straight to our apartment.
I didn't even think about the Littles
navigating the scene alone.
They weren't alone;
they had each other.

Exactly thirty minutes later,
Did you HEAR?!
Azalea screamed
as revitalized grief overran the apartment.
By then I was sitting on the couch,
biology book in my lap,
bowl of plantain chips beside me,
not digesting a word.

Liam jumped off the roof.

I was swiftly
taken back
to the second time
we saw Liam.
To when I first loved him.

He'd stalked us at Spriggs Park,

124

where we were playing frisbee with the Littles.
He'd walked up to us chest slightly less puffed,
after Freesia had shrunken him
just a week before on the park bench.
That day the look on his face
reminded me
of our dog Copper—
a begging,
dependent desire.

I'd looked away,
and Freesia
assumed it was her he was after.
I don't date white boys;
even my flower is native to Africa.
I nearly swallowed my bubblegum,
straddling
laugh out loud on one side,
horror on the other.
I looked at him,
nonplussed;
looked at her
and the word that came to me
when I replayed it into my journal
was *austere.*

Yet he pursued.
He met us at the park,
at the library,
at the pool
all summer.

She recited her refrain so much
that Liam started introducing himself as
Freesia's White Boy,
which always got at least a quarter
of a smile out of her.

Still,
my very first thought
when I heard
it was Liam
was,
Thank you, Jesus!
He's our third.
Freesia's safe.
All my sisters are safe.
Mom is safe.

I did think,
God forgive me.
But, not right away.

My three youngest sisters
were a host of tears.
Not the phony, ceremonial kind
derived from imagined sadness over the idea of a person.
These girls were mourning *our* loved one.

I would have stayed down
in the crowded street
to catch my sisters in their grief

if I had known that it was Liam.

Still, as they wailed,
I thanked Him,
repeatedly,
full of shame.

That faceless someone
was now Liam.
I could have feigned confusion,
but it would have been phony,
ceremonial,
derived from the idea of Liam
I'd held onto
in spite of what I knew.

Finally, I let who he really was
sink in.

And I became an island floating on top of their grief.

Liam was
the boy who'd taught us to fly.

He'd taken us to Preston Row,
the clam-tight
street with a cul-de-sac
that hung like a pendulum necklace
at the end of a very long, plunging neck.
No one ever leaves or returns,
he'd said the first time,

127

in an experimentally scary voice
that ended up sounding more like a shabby
attempt at sexy.
And we never did see a car moving on that street.

He taught us how to soar above
the decline.
Start at the top,
feet on pedals,
and push off.
Pump the pedals as fast as possible to the count of ten.
Count slowly, but not one-one-thousand slow.
Stop! Spread your feet wide.
Close your eyes.
Lift your hands to the sky.
Balance with your heart.

Birds set free.

We could all do some of it
but none of us as fearlessly
as Liam.
I'd watched
him once
from the edge of the pendulum.
I'd feigned rest before heading back up the hill.
Really I just wanted to climb back up
with him.
Legs out, eyes closed, arms
spread wide enough to hug the sky—
I couldn't have told anyone in words

what that look
on his face
meant.
I hadn't believed my eyes anyway.
It was a feeling—
that Liam was the one in need.
He created a weightlessness
for us, but
he remained leaden.

Liam was
someone we knew well enough
to qualify for death number three.
Surely.

He'd grown on us
and I liked him.
A lot.
I secretly like-liked him.
His naturally upturned eyelashes
and evergreen eyes,
cinnamon-colored hair,
his lips
pouted and puckered,
pale persimmon.
(Dahlia teased him that he wore lipstick.)
I marveled at how his skin stayed tan
from vacation after vacation.
His parents actually took him to the
Galapagos Islands.
He made us laugh

not with the gross jokes of most of the boys we knew;
Liam's jokes were smart—
unless he was flirting,
and then he was a lame boy again.
He teased the Littles,
taught them things
that an actual big brother would have.
That Daddy would have.
He raced them,
played Marco Polo with them in the pool,
and he never let them win at anything.
He wasn't ashamed
to be seen following
six poor, brown sisters
all over the city.

Mostly
he led us.

Late one night,
after a full day at the pool
with Liam,
Freesia had said dreamily,
It would have been nice to have had a brother.
I made a subtle sound
that could have been interpreted as agreement.
I knew then that, for real, she had no feelings
for him beyond friendship.
But our life was not <u>Little Women</u>.
I couldn't ever date a boy who had loved my sister.
So Liam was our *brother from another mother (and father)*.

The idea
of losing him sucked.
More than sucked.

But life sucked sometimes
and I'd rather it suck by
Liam killing himself
than by me losing one of my sisters
or Mom.
I would have taken his death over Daddy's,
if I'd had a choice in that.

I silenced the murmur
that my heart was chafing
into a fist-sized callous
like Freesia's.

When the Littles calmed down,
I reminded them we would have to tone down
our sadness for Mom.
Mom didn't know we'd spent unrestrained hours with a
boy.
Mom had spelled out rules about everything.
Longer than the decrees given to the Children of Israel
was her list

regarding boys.
We had mostly kept them;
Liam had been a stowaway in the apartment
only once.

131

We'd never, any of us, been alone with him;
we'd never been to his home.
None of us claimed him as a boyfriend.

Somehow, though,
keeping company with Liam felt like disobedience.
We were in ambiguous territory
as far as the rules were concerned.
We weren't exactly sure what Mom would have done
but felt certain there was a high probability
of even stricter rules.

Amaryllis and Dahlia nodded solemnly,
but Azalea let out one last, dismal
whimper before heading to the bathroom
to wash the evidence away.

By the time Freesia and Zinnia unlocked the door
and appeared at the threshold,
the rest of us sat crouched
or criss-cross-applesauce
or lying down
over textbooks, worksheets, study guides
and a picture book.
Not a single word read or picture seen.
I looked up with a quick, casual
Hey,
and looked back down at my vocabulary list.
Mom had been given a used SAT prep book
from a co-worker.

SAT vocab was survivable;
the thought of Liam dead
was not.
Freesia's presence pummeled my conscious.
She didn't even like him,
I lied to myself.

It took me longer than it should have to register Freesia's
disintegration.
I was pretending to read the next word before I realized
she hadn't moved further into the apartment
or closed the door
or breathed.

I released my eyes from the book.
Lifting them to Freesia
felt like the stories you hear of grandmas
lifting cars off their run-over grandchildren.

Zinnia held Freesia up,
hunched and overburdened.
A gaping crater had quaked
dead-center down the middle
of Freesia's customarily steely face,
and out of it erupted
a misery so raw
it tormented me to look at her.

And so I looked away.

Zinnia, realizing I would not be coming to the rescue,

had no choice
but to let Freesia fall to a heap on the floor.
Zinnia's eyes bore the word *traitor* into mine,
a permanent tattoo,
a self-conscious filter through which I might always see
myself.

The Littles abandoned their studies
and ran to Freesia with comforting words and touches.

I'm the traitor?
I wanted to shriek.
Didn't they remember that
ever since Daddy left, Freesia had been a statue?
And now, for Liam,
the white boy she'd scorned
she turned to rubble.

But the Littles arrowed stern side-glares at me
between *tuk-tuks* and *shhhhs*
to Freesia.
So I humbled myself the way Ma Moore
was always advising Freesia.

It took me a millisecond
to box my grief for Liam.
To throw it away.

I walked over and touched her
and my touch poured the strength
into her the others had failed to produce.

I led her to her bed and helped her to undress
and lifted her PJs over her head and her arms into the
sleeves
and tucked her in.

We ate dinner in silence,
all of us thinking about Liam
and Freesia
and astounded that maybe there had
been the possibility
of a Liam and Freesia
all along.

RESCUE

The night Daddy came back
we were in the house again,
rooms shared
two-by-two again,
but Mom slept alone.
We could still see the garden
from the kitchen sink window
and smell lilacs or honeysuckle
when it was open
in summer or spring.
The four Black Knight
butterfly bushes
that sat under the family room window drew
ruby-throated hummingbirds
and spring azures,
but we took everything for granted.

Spring grinned outside;
inside, we gritted our teeth and shivered.
The flames in the fireplace
cast dancing fairies
across every surface.
Five hot chocolate
mugs topped
five mosaic glass coasters,
sprinkled atop
hearth,
coffee table,

side tables.

Just before we heard the doorbell,
I sat on the loveseat reading,
lamenting my empty mug
and eyeing Zinnia's,
half full.
She lay across the other couch asleep,
covered in a quilt Ma Moore made for Dahlia.
I couldn't grasp why it had no place
there.
Her cocoa legs spilled out,
falling over themselves
and the arm
of the couch.
Every once in a while, a foot
would twitch or swing forward,
distracting me
with its spontaneity.

Daddy's voice wouldn't allow my annoyance.
If something can distract you that easily,
you aren't really focused.

The Littles lay on the floor,
thread amongst themselves
like a mixed up
pile of chocolate yarn,
watching TV.
All of us in PJs.

Freesia and Mom were unseen.

The doorbell rang,
and from somewhere came the knowledge
that Mom was upstairs napping
and Freesia upstairs sulking.

So I answered,
greeting my Daddy—
my living, breathing, no-longer dead Daddy—
in the foyer
of our
home.

In the living room,
it had been drafty grey
with bursts of warm orange.
Here, though, the sun
beamed in through twelve smokey
glass panels
in mahogany
double doors.
Honeysuckle syrup sailed
in with each waft of the door,
inviting us outside
to the promise of
perspiration-inspiring play,
so familiar.

My joy must have vocalized—
How else would my sisters have known?

A mad dash
of girls suddenly dressed
in dance leotards and soccer uniforms,
dresses and jean shorts.

All of us pressing
in and pushing
out,
elbows and shoulders,
knees folding over
overlapping toes,
a unit.

Like always
Daddy's smile took up
his entire face.
His spicy aftershave,
the bass in his voice,
his bicep made of steel
induced
my eyes to water,
my teeth to chatter,
my fingers to squeeze
him just a bit tighter.
He existed.
He didn't have to speak
for all of us to feel
everything reattach,
all
anchored.

Until—
Where's Freesia?
Five flowers' petals
fluttering in his wind,
reverent,
no space left around
him,
and still he missed
the lost one.
Even before he missed Mom.

Like the father scanning the road for his prodigal son,
Daddy eyed the staircase that led to Freesia's heart.

I raised my face,
looked up
all the way through the ceiling
to the floor right above our heads
into the room we shared,
Freesia and me.
Stale with the jaded fog and
fetid stench
of her animus.

If he could have seen,
would he have chosen
to leave the five
for the one?
But I reached
his eyes and knew
he would chase her,

find her,
retrieve her,
add her to his orbit—
no matter what.

Mom entered then,
threadbare,

and his smile

rewove her.

She reached out to him
and we all fell away,
unnatural,
like spring
giving
way to fall.
Inevitable
because fall still comes.

Their arms fused,
then their palms and knuckles,
thumbs,
until they began
and ended
together.

Joined,
they left our sunlight
and climbed the stairs

into darkness.

Mom turned back once.
Her face had rewound
two years
to before.

I had forgotten…

Her square face,
pointed even before she was twenty pounds
underweight.
How the angular cheekbones peaked
atop her cheeks even when she wasn't smiling.
The slight divot under each one
like a sculpture;
her flawless umber skin.
Daddy said her face could
sell any beauty product on the market.
Her sleepy grey eyes,
twin genetic anomalies.

I had forgotten
that Mom was beautiful.

She's art.
But I never fell for a pretty face.
I go for smart.
Your mom is brilliant,
but what set her apart
was the love.

No beauty,
no degree in the world
could make me feel
what I feel when she looks at me,
looks at the six of you.

Daddy didn't look back at all,
just kept climbing toward his missing flower,
but I could see his face
still smiling.

Amaryllis told me once
the Scottish have four hundred
words for snow.

Daddy had smiled three different smiles
just since our reunion.

The one for us
without Freesia.
The one for Mom.
The one with the resolve
to rescue Freesia.
Daddy always found a way
through everything
with some caliber of joy,
like an exceptional kind of GPS.
If we tried to name all of Daddy's smiles
I bet we'd get to at least two hundred.

The others and I

stood at the foot of the stairs,
listening to
swords clash
and shrieks rear like beasts,
the once transparent ceiling
now caked with ash.
The remnants of something burning
explained the heat emanating
from above,
that swelter barbing our skin
in a way terribly opposite the springtime
deliverance.

I sensed I needed to pray
for my parents
and my sister,
for victory.

But prayer,
like Ma Moore's quilt,
didn't belong in our house.

And then
the noise
the heat
the battle
died.

Life above
seemed impossible.

I could hear their breathing,
though, and the creak of their footsteps.
And just before I saw them come
to the top of the stairs—

Iris! Iris! What is it? Did you see Daddy?
Freesia shaking me.
Through the slit of my left eye,
she scowled at me.
I kept my right eye slammed shut,
resisting the call
to reality.

Who voluntarily abandons a dream fulfilled?

We had prayed every night
for months when he first died.
Please, God, please let us see him in our dreams, at least.
Please?

I woke up in the mornings
knowing God hadn't said *Yes*
in answer to my prayers,
but He might have said *Yes* to Free.
Hope and dread—
for Daddy to come to me,
for him not to go to her instead.
For him to come to both of us
or neither of us.

Some days we put off asking

one another until our PJs
were on for the next night of hope
and dread.
And since I knew Freesia could not,
I never told her that I was able to hear him.
What if she had seen
him and kept it from me
for the same reason?

Hiding the dream would not be easy.
She'd heard me call out to him.

My cheeks displayed the evidence of
rejoicing,
answered prayer,
mourning,
renewed loss.

Tears relentless
as the hearse that had carried Daddy's body,
determined.

Did you? Did you see him?

Her eyes are Daddy's eyes—
so dark you can't separate the pupils
from the irises—
lovely
identical black holes.
Stars
so strong that nothing

can escape.

The rest of us have irises
not quite grey like Mom's,
not as dark as Daddy's.
Muted.

Daddy told me once our irises
control the amount of light
entering our eyes.
He said I'm named after a flower,
but I ended up more like the part
of the eye—
a gatekeeper of the family's light.
God, in His infinite wisdom
made you both things—
a tender flower
and a sentry,
a keeper of our light.

Daddy rarely talked about God.
Before he died, we weren't churchgoers.
That's the hardest part for me,
knowing that being a Christian
might mean I don't get to see Daddy when I die.
Maybe he didn't make it.
There's a chance, though.
Ma Moore says,
I think we'll be surprised at who we see
up there and who we don't.
Only God can judge.

147

Maybe that's why I could stomach
the thought of Liam
dying.
I knew for sure he'd make it to heaven.

The last time we saw him
before he jumped,
we'd spent the day at Spriggs Park.
It had rained through a month of weekends
and it was soccer season,
so we hadn't seen him in weeks.

But that last day,
the sun was out
and his game was early in the morning.
We met him at noon with a picnic basket
full of lunch and a blanket that was waterproof on one
side
from before Daddy died.

Liam brought dessert—
a cinch bag full of candy and seven sodas.
When the Littles wanted to play,
Freesia went with them.
And Liam, wasting no time, said he was ready
to invite Jesus into his heart,
to make Him his Savior.
Together we sat cross-legged on the picnic blanket,
facing one another and holding hands.
With bowed heads and closed eyes,

he repeated
The Sinner's Prayer
line by line
after me.
At the end, he looked into my eyes the way I'd imagined,
and I enjoyed the notion of him loving me
instead of Freesia.
Later that night when I replayed it,
I admitted
that probably he was looking right through me
toward Jesus
and the rest of his life
saved.

I also thought
about how God intervenes every day
and how when we're not focused on Him,
we miss it.
Freesia almost never voluntarily entertained
the Littles alone.
I did.
Liam did.
Would Liam have asked me to pray
with him if she hadn't left us alone?
What would it take for Freesia to be next?
I knew I needed to pray and trust
Him to speak to her.
Still, I kept making it a mission, like it was up to me
to do the right things to make it happen.
As if God needed my help.

Even if Daddy's not there
and Freesia never made it,
I still wanted to go to heaven.

There was a song we heard on the radio
all the time at first, and then just sometimes,
as songs on the radio go.
The singer claimed
unfailing loyalty;
promising to walk even through hell
if it came to that.

There wasn't anyone
I was willing to walk through hell
with.

So when Freesia asked me, I told her,
I saw him.
Because her eyes
hadn't held on
to anything since Liam jumped,
He rescued you.

I had to start believing He would.
Freesia didn't cry.
Not when Mom told us
in a voice that was as dead as Daddy was.
Not when she drove
us to the funeral home
so we could see our daddy
before the viewing.

Not when we went a second time
the next day
after we'd begged her because
none of us had ever gone a day without seeing him.
Even a cold, stiff, serious-faced, off-color Daddy
was better than no Daddy at all.

Not at the funeral
with Mom's muted cry
scaring us more than if she had screamed.
I wanted her to just scream already;
give me permission to scream, too.

Instead, gloppy tears slumped over themselves
out of eyes that failed to blink.
I remember thinking then that if God
had created
tiny windshield wipers for eyes
I could turn Mom's on.
An authentic titter nearly crept from my soul,
a giggle at my own Daddy's funeral!

I pinched myself hard with my left pointer and thumb
under my right arm, just near my armpit—
that secret, tender spot where Mom pinches
us when we misbehave in public.
And I remembered a commercial
advertising some medication for people who laugh
when they are supposed to be crying.
Maybe I had that?
Because how else?

Mom's tears formed tributaries on her cheeks,
running into
rivers of snail-like slime
dribbling from her nose,
unwiped.
The mucus formed a sickening puddle
on Mom's hunter green dress
in the space between her breasts,
which should have horrified her
but didn't.

We all wore green because it was Daddy's favorite.
He called it the color of life.

Freesia didn't cry.
As the rest of us sniffled and sobbed and blubbered,
Freesia never cried.

I remembered then what Daddy said
and for the first time ever, I felt sorry for my sister.
I felt stronger than her.
I felt like her protector.
I prayed she wouldn't cry,
convinced that she would die
if even one tear fell.

As Freesia settled back into her bed
with the knowledge I had dreamt of Daddy,
I thought of
my school friend, Arad,

and started praying I could somehow teach Freesia
just by being with her
to unveil
and unguard.
I could convince her to drop her weapons.
I could re-arm her with the tenderness
of Jesus.

I knew it could happen in degrees so minuscule
I wouldn't notice.
One day she'd look exactly the same,
but she'd speak a different language,
and we'd all know new armor had been
put on.

POINT OF VIEW

Weeks after our move
we did an internet search
at the library
and learned
that Daddy's brain died
in four to six minutes.
The rest
of his body lasted three days.

All six
of us had huddled
over that library computer.
the day after
Amaryllis asked at breakfast,
How long does it take to die?

It had been six months,
then,
since Daddy had died.

We were already in the apartment,
already at our new schools.
We had just started to attend
Grace Walk.

Mom had swept us into our new life
so briskly
I wondered if maybe she'd always

had a closet in her mind
and a what-if broom
in that closet
just in case.
I wondered if Daddy would have been so quick
to give it all up.

Liam asked me once,
after only a few months of knowing us,
how Daddy had died.
His question
pulled the ground from under me
with its straightforwardness.
It felt insulting,
but then it was refreshing,
too,
because he'd wanted to know
and he'd asked.

I told him the story,
which I'd never told.
I'd cried
and he'd known how long to hug me,
when to let go,
when to rub my back,
when to look at me,
and when to look
away.
His neck formed the perfect space
for me to angle my face into.
He smelled like oranges and the Christmas trees

Daddy always brought
home on December 13
and sweat.
He whispered one lie
over and over.
It's okay. It's okay. It's okay.

The day Daddy died,
we were having dinner outside
because it had been cold and rainy
for ten days straight
and on the eleventh day
God sent sun so intense
it dried our deck,
picnic table and chairs,
and raised the outside temperature by thirty-five degrees
overnight.

Daddy announced that we would cook out
and started chopping meat and pulling seasonings
off the built-in Lazy Susan
in the cupboard,
four at a time.

Mom went out to do some last-minute Easter shopping
and to grab the cocoa and butter
for the brownies Azalea wanted to bake
and the ice cream Daddy had to have
to go with them.
Daddy could not eat cake, cookies, or brownies
without ice cream.

Mom grabbed her keys and her purse.
Don't wait for me! You know how I get
when it's just me and my debit card.

And we did.
When Mom went out alone,
she was liable to drive past the cinema,
remember a movie she wanted to see,
buy a ticket for one and enjoy it alone.
Mom could spend the entire day shopping.
None of us ever complained.

Mom was home all week.
We only got Daddy for two days.

Daddy cooked chicken and beef kabobs on the grill.
I had cut up all the onion and peppers.
We poked the mushrooms on whole.
There was the promise of warm brownies and ice cream
later.
Zinnia cut up a fruit salad in a glass bowl
that Mom and Daddy bought in Italy
on their honeymoon.
Freesia cut flowers from the garden to fill a vase.
I filled Mom's crystal pitcher with ice water.

We ate with plastic utensils on paper plates
and drank from plastic cups.
Freesia cringed at the mismatch
of glass, crystal, paper and plastic,

called it *Faux Fabulous.*
Daddy's laugh burst through her annoyance.

We all sat down and Amaryllis said the blessing.
That's the thing I wish we'd forgotten that day
of all days,
just that once.

We had thanked God,
and He'd taken Daddy away.

We all dug in
in a jumble that was reserved
for when Mom was gone—
talking with hands covering mouths full of food,
wiping those full mouths with the backs of those same
hands,
napkins left untouched.
Loud slurps of water.
A big, open-mouthed belch from Dahlia.
Pieces of meat bitten directly from the skewers
or plucked off with greasy fingers,
those same greasy fingers ignoring
the serving spoon and lifting slices of pineapple
and slivers of apple from the glass bowl.

Mom liked us to hold the skewer with one hand
and use our forks or knives to slide the morsels off.
When she was around, every dish
had a serving utensil.
Every burp was done quietly, with mouth closed.

Napkins were placed on laps and used to dab mouths.
There was absolutely no talking with food in mouths
except when she had to tell us
no talking with food in our mouths
with food in her mouth.
I have to tell you while you're doing it or you won't learn.

The food always tasted better
with greasy hands and full mouths
and the occasional belch.
We all soaked in the much-missed sun
as we gobbled and slurped
and laughed and talked with our mouths full of food,
reaching over one another to get seconds and thirds.

Daddy's voice boomed
carefree and fun.

Then he sat still,
his face like a glacier
frozen in some kind of assessment,
and then his eyes moved clockwise
slow as the second hand
for as long as it took
to see all of us
one last time.
Then they bulged.
His throat made a collapsed kind of unbreathing sound.
His hands clutched his neck like he was trying to speed
the process along.

He leaned backward,
sending his legs up,
lifting the table and
scattering our meal, utensils
cups, napkins, plates,
overturning and cracking Mom's crystal pitcher.
The bowl from Italy shattered into pieces
infinitesimal.
Amaryllis sang *Oooooowwwww!*
She didn't realize
that the pitcher would no longer matter
that day
or ever.

Daddy fell to the ground,
onto his back
with a thud.
The rock that his head settled
on first soaked in
and then began to seep
his blood.

Only then did Freesia jump to action.

Call 911!
Help me!
She seemed to leap over
the overturned table
to Daddy's side.
We have to try to get it out!
Call 911!

She opened his mouth and used her fingers to search the
back of his throat.
Help me turn him over!
She tried to get him in a position to do the Heimlich.
But Daddy was 6'4", 225 pounds.
When that failed,
she beat his back frantically.
Help me!
Call 911!
And louder,
Oh, God! Help us! Help us! Help us!
We have to get it out!
Help me!
She alternated between sticking her fingers into his
mouth
and trying to use her fists to push down and upward
in the middle of Daddy's chest.
Oh, God. Please!

I don't know how long
before help
came.
Two minutes,
two days,
both entirely plausible.

From the distance I heard the ambulance
get closer and closer,
commotion inside the house,
and people running toward us.
Zinnia led them.

She had called 911.
She directed them outside,
but she stayed just inside the house,
refusing to pass through the
sliding glass door
into our terrible parallel universe.

Freesia and I stood side-by-side,
holding hands.
I took turns watching them work on Daddy
and searching the yard for my sisters.
I counted them over and over again,
every couple of minutes.

Freesia by my side.
Zinnia at the door.
Dahlia and Azalea behind the picnic table.
Dahlia's head hidden under her arms
like a pointless school drill.
Azalea's eyes as big as Daddy's had bulged
when they'd been open.
Amaryllis crouched behind a lilac bush,
her back to us, rocking slightly from side-to-side.
My feet cemented in place,
unable to go to her,
to hold her steady.

How many minutes were the paramedics there,
trying to get Daddy to live?
Long enough for Mom to come home,
screaming our names through the house

until she finally reached the backyard,
stepped into our reality,
took in the scene.
I watched her survey and count
and count again.
Only when she found Amaryllis
did she drop to her knees next to Daddy.

Questions streamed from her mouth in a way
that reminded me of Amaryllis'
endless pouring of ponderings
and we treated her exactly like Amaryllis—
no answers.
Not because we didn't know,
but because we couldn't.

He hasn't moved.
His chest hasn't moved.
He isn't breathing.
How long can a person go without breathing?
How long has it been?

Mom went with the ambulance to the hospital
with Daddy.
She jutted her chin toward Amaryllis,
told Freesia and me to collect
everyone,
to leave the food,
the broken glass,
the blood.
Everything.

163

To go inside.
To lock all the doors.
To turn the television on,
something appropriate.
NO LOCAL NEWS.
To wait for her call.

We did everything she said
and also turned
the television on in our parents' bedroom
to local news
and took turns, Freesia
and I,
listening for Daddy's name.
Daddy was important enough
to make the news.
But no news came.

Much later,
when we had given up hope
that Mom would call us that night
or ever
and realized that we didn't really want her to,
we turned both televisions
off.
We piled six across
in Mom and Daddy's king-sized bed,
no one wanting to sleep next to Dahlia
because sometimes she still wet the bed
and we hadn't been able to find any of her nighttime
diapers.

We put her on the end.
Zinnia next to her.

I took the other end of the bed,
furthest from Dahlia
because pee spreads.
During the night
for hours
comforter tugged
bed springs creaked.
The deep, rhythmic breaths of rest finally
took over.
I felt wholly abandoned.
Then feet shuffled.
I opened
my eyes to Freesia's
just centimeters away,
her kneeling beside the bed.

How did you know all that stuff to do? I asked.

She whispered back, *What stuff?*

*Flipping him over and trying to get the food out and beating on
his back and the Heimlich? Where did you learn that?*

*Me? That was you. I stood there useless. You tried to save
Daddy.*

No.

Unh unh.

That was definitely you!
Three of my sisters chimed in, all at the same time.
coming clean,
their sleep feigned.
Their voices a symphony of revelation.

Me? But I don't know anything about saving someone.

Then from Amaryllis,
None of us do.

Later, I thought about calling
on God over and over
to help us
even before I knew Him.
He'd answered me—
not with keeping Daddy alive,
but with Ma Moore,
and with Grace,
and with Liam,
and survival.

DISOBEDIENCE

Liam had been inside the apartment
only once.

He'd shown up on the Tuesday
of spring break, and the Littles
all squealed and jumped and clapped,
happy to see him.
Did you get left home alone?
Freesia smirked, hands on hips.
He was supposed to be on vacation.

Plans changed. Dad's company had some snafu.
Mom was relieved.
She really couldn't afford to take the time off.
So, what's on the agenda today?

We were doing our usual—
park, library, nothing.
Idle minutes and hours spent
hoping for some excitement
that wasn't too exciting.

How about we finally settle up our Spelling Smash bet?
Ever since Liam
won the Spelling Smash Tournament
at his school,
Freesia had been itching to outplay
him.

167

Bet!
Liam's grin stalled my heart
for the trillionth time.
Freesia's dutiful pinch
restored it.

Why are you always pinching me?
I asked her one night
when I noticed a quarter-sized bruise
on the back of my thigh.
To erase that stupid stuck-on smile
from your face
when Loverboy's around.
She'd shrugged.
And I was grateful.

Let's go.
The two of them began to move toward the building,
toward the apartment
as if it was the most natural thing,
and the Littles followed them
as if we invited Liam up to the apartment
every day.

Wait! Guys?
I whispered it.
Then repeated myself, louder.
No one stopped.
They were like kangaroos
and me, a sloth.

Up in the apartment,
the Spelling Smash board was already out;
Liam and Freesia
already set up with seven tiles each,
rearranging them competitively
on their wooden tile racks.

If the rest of my sisters were worried
about Mom walking in
and killing us,
they were shockingly sedate.

I watched Liam closely for signs of
pity or disdain
at our tiny place.
Nothing from him, either.

My distress began to dissipate
with the clacking of tiles,
the playful trash talk,
the Littles' giggles,
the undeniable innocence
of a board game.

I didn't hear the jingle of the keys,
the bolt disengage.
The push forward
deterred
the faint voice of Mom,
Girls, let me in.

But my sisters did.

They were fast into action
before the panic hit me.

Freesia had attached the security bolt
for just such a situation.

It seemed they had all been through the drill.
I alone stood dumbstruck.
This was not a drill.

Freesia walked calmly to the door
and slowly detached the chain lock.
Zinnia went into the kitchen and began making dinner.
Miraculously, she started on step five.
Azalea led Liam to one of the bedrooms and closed the
door.
Amaryllis and Dahlia grabbed books and lounged on the
couch to read.

The Spelling Smash board obediently sat in place.
Everyone had known just what to do.

As Mom walked in the apartment,
I listed toward Zinnia to help with dinner
to give my hands something to do
besides wring uncontrollably.
I'm so glad you girls are using that security bolt!
But what on earth are you doing inside?
I thought for sure you'd be enjoying this weather.

Oh, Spelling Smash. Who's playing?
These words are impressive.

Iris and I, but Iris had help.
Zale wasn't feeling well, so we came home.
Freesia grabbed the chemical caddy
and a couple of rags
from under the kitchen sink
and began wiping things.

Oh.
Mom said as she headed toward the room
to check on Azalea.
I nearly peed myself
and bulged my eyes at Freesia.
What in the world?
You led her right to Zale!

But the only sounds coming from the room were
murmurs—
Mom's exhausted concern,
Azalea's feigned illness—
and then Mom was out again.
I don't think it's anything serious.
Keep an eye on her.
I'm going to try to catch a nap.

She went into the other room
and shut the door.
Seconds later we heard Miles Davis
lulling her to sleep.

Freesia grabbed a sheet of paper and a pencil
and knelt to draw a map of the Spelling Smash board.
So we can continue another time.
She winked at me.

Azalea brought Liam out,
and led him to the door,
and he left just as unremarkably
as he'd come,
but not before getting Freesia's attention,
aiming his pointer and middle fingers at his eyes
and then her,
without saying out loud,
I'm watching you!

We all knew there was no way Freesia would ever cheat.
She was going to beat Liam fair
and square if she was going to beat him at all.

The next day,
the Spelling Smash board came with us
to Spriggs Park,
the tiles were restored based on Freesia's map,
and Freesia
did beat Liam
by 52 points.

SUPERNATURAL

By some miracle
Liam did not die.

He'd jumped from a five-story building
and survived,
but Daddy died from choking.

Updates on Liam's recovery
broadcast every night
on local news.
The entire city was praying for him.
Daddy hadn't been mentioned in the news once.

If I were in charge, I'd want people to know
you really can die from choking.
Everyone already knows you can die from jumping
off a building.

At Grace, the quilt ministry made him a quilt
and we all prayed over it,
tying a tiny ribbon knot for each prayer.

When Freesia spoke up, offering
to take the quilt to Liam's family,
ripples of *Amen* and *God bless you, Child*
were drowned out
by my wave of panic.

We couldn't go
to Liam
without Mom finding out
we'd skipped school—
not all of us.

And there was no way the Littles
would let us go
without them.

These were the days when we needed Ma Moore
the most
but she fell ill, missed church
four Sundays in a row.

Freesia couldn't rest.
The quilt squatted,
folded squarely in airtight
plastic wrapping,
hidden in plain sight among our household linens,
begging to be caught.

She pestered
me with repeated pleading.
I told her, *No.*
Definitive.

At night, she tossed and turned
in bed and begged
me with every sigh
and gaze unspoken.

She smothered me in guilt,
her exhales emitting agony
like morning breath.

I convinced myself that if she could see
Liam,
she would see a miracle unfold.
By then it was clear he might
actually survive.
If she could say goodbye to doubt,
Maybe she could say goodbye to Daddy, too,
and the bitterness,
swaddled in those goodbyes,
would leave space in her for God.

The worst Mom
could do was give us more rules
she wouldn't be home to enforce.

I pretended to go to school.
Freesia played sick.
We took the bus to the hospital,
taking turns holding the quilt
as if the magic in it could only be
handled for limited amounts of time.

Ma Moore had warned us.
Back when she had been well,
when the church had prepared
a different prayer quilt

for a different sick child.
Cancer.
I want you to remember that this quilt
is not magic.
We prayed over it, but our prayers hold no power
absent from God.
Just don't want you getting confused
as to who all the glory's owed to.

This quilt is meant to remind the family
that people have prayed,
continue to pray unceasingly,
a symbol of the power of collective agreement
within His holy will.

Still, the power of it was undeniable.

Liam lay
in the same hospital
that Daddy had been taken to.
The best trauma hospital in the city,
which is really not an endorsement
for where you want your loved one to have to be.

I grabbed Freesia's hand
and she looked at me,
but I could not look at her,
so I looked straight ahead
to the doors we had to walk through.
Down at the feet of those who trudged
ahead.

I wondered how Liam's parents would
greet us.
Even now, a dull pain pulses
when I see fathers and daughters
together.
Here Liam's parents would have to face
two teenagers
healthy,
whole,
unbroken.

I said a prayer for them
(I hadn't even thought of them before),
and I made a promise
to always pray for the ones
left behind.

Inside,
the hospital expanded
and nearly split like too-small pants.
Too fat with families and friends
frenzied in
barely bridled mania,
breaking out in cold sweats.
Why do they keep hospitals
and schools so frigid?

It's probably to keep the germ count down.
Freesia, ever practical.

We looked for a sign.
We had no idea where to go,
whom to ask.
In the movies,
only family could be told anything.

Being out of place was our specialty.
We reflexively headed toward obscurity;
sitting in a far corner.
Faith told me a sign would come.

Liam's mother
(he actually called her *Mother*)
stood by a vending machine.
I knew she was Liam's mother
as soon as her eyes touched mine.

His eyes were hers—
same size,
same shape,
same radiation
but not that same otherworldly green;
they were diluted,
a sparkling hazel
ensconced by endless eyelashes.
As long and curly as his,
they tickled my ears the same way,
whispered that they really saw me.

The rest of Liam's mother lay in wait,
the sprinkle of cinnamon freckles that powdered

her cheeks and forehead,
exactly the same cinnamon that capped Liam's head
and umbrellaed his eyes.
Auburn spiral curls bobbed as she approached,
one million miniature pogo sticks.
Her tawny skin ambushed me.

She found us hunched in our hiding place.
I stood first and Freesia followed,
grabbing my hand and squeezing my fingers.
I squeezed hers back.
Liam is Black?

It made so much sense
then
that Liam hadn't molded
himself squarely into the inheritance
his skin tone afforded.
He'd confided in me once
that many white people feel free
to make racist comments
when they think there's no Black person in the room.
And because Freesia wasn't within
earshot, I'd confessed that I once sat through
an entire conversation at recess
about how nasty white people are—
how they don't use washcloths to bathe,
and how they don't wash their hands
after using the bathroom,
how they let cats walk on their countertops,
and on

179

and on
and on.

It was cleansing,
that moment
when we'd each shared our
race's dirty secrets.
But Liam was Black all along.

Are you the Flower Sisters.
No inquiry in her inflection.
Freesia's intake of breath
expanded even my lungs—
all the answer Liam's mother hadn't needed.

Please come with me.
Everyone knows you can smile
without that smile ever reaching your eyes.
Never before had I seen someone smile
with only their eyes.

We walked with her, bewildered.
Entered the elevator that her graceful, sandy hand
directed us into.
She remained close
but turned her back to press the button
to lift us off
to Liam.

As the elevator doors opened,
an older woman,

skin just a shade darker,
a tearful mass,
approached us.
Liam's mother reached for this woman,
took her in,
her deep auburn spirals drifting
side-to-side as she talked.
Her head in a constant, slow motion
shake
as if she refused to be an accessory
to the terror-strike,
but without conviction.

The four of us continued down the hall,
passed the nurse's station,
where Liam's mom made eye contact
and the nurses nodded.

To the left,
a room
that later I would not be able to describe.
It must have been Liam in the bed,
although we couldn't see him,
covered and affixed
to bed,
bandages,
tubes and machines.

Liam's father appeared
hazy,
a ghost in the corner.

I peeked at him,
hunched over,
only a glimpse of his eyes
downcast,

forget-me-not blue.
I couldn't see anything that had passed
from him to Liam except
that his ivory skin mixed with her bronze
created Liam's beige,
like desert stone.
Liam was Black.

The sterile room sagged
with the force of us
all collapsing into vigil
at once.
Silence descended
like a noxious gas,
all eyes on Liam.

Liam's mother watched her son
with a look of protection on her face
so fierce
it reminded me of talons.

Finally, she spoke.
You can talk to him.
He can hear us.
I'm sure he's wishing he could rush to the park
to see his Flowers.

He's been cooped up with all of us old people,
rattling off about the weather.
But I know you girls must have
updates to give him.
She pleaded with us.

His grandmother sat next to his dad,
and began unwrapping the quilt.
I hadn't even seen it change hands.
The crinkling of plastic barely audible
under the beeping and whooshing of machines.

Freesia walked to Liam,
stood by his head,
beckoned me.
I walked slowly to the other side of him.
Only fragments of skin showed
through bandages and blanket.
Without asking,
she put her hand over his hand,
and I flinched.
She kissed the bandage on his forehead.

Liam's mother and grandmother
wept,
harmonizing
like the saddest song.

I wasn't going to even touch him.
But then Freesia moved her hand away
and I was suspended,

looking down at the first boy
I'd ever loved.

What if his mother found out
I'd been relieved when I heard it was him?
That I hadn't consoled Freesia?
Hadn't allowed myself to miss him
or even cry for him once?

Soon a tender moaning mixed with his mother's
and his grandmother's.
Imposing,
undeserving,
tears spilled onto him,
tainting the truth.

Was I really happy
when I thought Liam would die?
If not happy, then approving
that it would be him?

Freesia's presence took hold
of my shoulders,
pushing back.
But I resisted, pulled forward,
bent over,
seized
my first kiss,
dry and cracked.

We're here, Liam.

Freesia's voice
pulled me out of my trance,
separated our lips,
levitated my upper half.
I stood straight, but couldn't take my eyes off him.

And Freesia's voice continued,
steady as Freesia always was.
We brought you a prayer quilt
the ladies at church made for you.
Everyone who prayed over it tied a little knot
in the ribbons.
I tried to count the knots,
but there are too many.
The whole city wants you to live.

The Littles are all worried about you.
They want to see you.
Zinnia made the soccer team.
Amie won the spelling bee.
Azalea wrote you a letter, but I couldn't bring it.
They don't know we're here.
You know they would have wanted to come.
They'll never forgive us,
Dahlia especially.
Why did you do this?
Was it me?
I'll never forgive myself
for pretending I didn't like you
if you don't get better.
Even though I know you know

I do like you and always have.
I wanted you to think you weren't important to me.
I don't know why.
A single tear.
And now I guess we both know what Iris pretended.
A smirk.
But if you get better, Liam,
you can be my brother.
You've always been our brother.
Well, I guess not Iris's.
We need you.
We all need you.

She squeezed his hand
and I flinched.

It was my turn to talk,
but I couldn't be like Freesia.
I couldn't joke with him or make him promises.

Why did you do this?
Was all I could get out.
Because even though I could look back and recall
his wounded features,
I couldn't look past
the two-parent home,
the private school,
the fancy vacations,
the good looks,
the straight A's,
the soccer stardom,

to see any *why*.

His mother came to me,
took me into her arms,
reached across the bed to Freesia.
I felt the slight tug
as Freesia accepted her hand.
You didn't do this.
In fact, I think you kept him alive.
I can't thank you enough.
He'll survive.
We will all survive.

I don't know how long we stayed
that first visit.
We walked
back out
into tepid daylight,
leaving Liam with his family
and feeling a part of them.

We rode the bus back,
spent.
Conveying our feelings
through a network of hand squeezing—
like the old days.
Both weary,
both dazed.
But also content.

One defiant move,

like a raft,
forged its way
against the current,
across the moat, the rivalry
that separated us.

For once
Freesia did not say
I told you so.
I knew she'd been right
and she knew I knew.

By the time we got to Brooks Street,
everything that needed to be pressed
out of us had been.
Still, our hands would not uncouple.
Our arms swung back and forth,
our lips posed in almost smiles.

At the apartment,
we tiptoed through the door,
even though we weren't expecting anyone
to be home.

From the threshold we heard
Mom sigh from a chair in the kitchen.
She moved to stand but remained seated,
eyeing us with the caution
of someone being approached by two large,
unfamiliar dogs.
After an hour-long minute,

188

she slowly stood,
maintaining eye contact
with us both.
She came to us,
her arms out
in indecision.
Pommel or embrace?

Where in the world have you girls been?
I got a call from the schools while I was at work.
And then I came here,
thinking you were both sick.
This is vacation time I'm using.
I was about to call the police.
This isn't like you two.
Is it?
Not rhetorical.
She really didn't know us anymore.
Her fault.

A hasty string of words
left my mouth,
phrases we'd come up with last night,
mostly Freesia's.

That boy on the news,
William Glenn,
is our friend.
Our best friend.
We decided at the last minute
to visit him.

We didn't ask because we knew
you would say no.
But we love him.
And then strung together in desperation.
AndtheLittlescanneverknow.

Her arms landed on embrace,
and then Mom summoned us to the couch,
her dark hand
as delicate and strong
as Liam's mother's.
Who is this friend?

And all of it erupted,
smoldering liquid
from Freesia's lips
this time,
but my words
exactly.

Mom sat statuesque,
listening to my words
in Freesia's voice,
her angular face unreadable.

Even after Freesia finished in a gasp
and looked to me for approval,
which I stamped for her in the form
of a verbose hand squeeze,
Mom didn't move,
didn't speak,

didn't breathe.

If she was overwhelmed,
her face did not incriminate.
If she was angry,
she concealed it well.
She must have been hurt
to discover
so much about daughters
that were once the heart beneath her ribs.

Mom used to greet us at the door
with warm fruit muffins—
pureed fruit
because Freesia didn't like them chunky.
She'd interrogate us about our day at school,
asking questions like
Who were you kind to today?
What clarifying questions did you ask your teacher?
Which child in your class do you think is most misunderstood?
She allowed our passions
and attended every exhibition of our talents.
She made us finish out a season of any activity we asked
to do,
even if it meant months of listening
to us whine about how much we loathed that activity.
She knew our favorite colors and animals and songs and
outfits.
Two years ago we were her life's work.

Now we have friends she doesn't know,

friends who jump from buildings.
We skip school to visit them in the hospital.

I'm sorry about your friend.
I wish I had known.
I'm also sorry we're at this place
where you feel you cannot trust
me to make decisions in your best interest;
where you feel I don't truly listen to you.
I wish you would have asked me.
I wish I could say with certainty
that I would have let you.
I wish so many things for us…

And in that moment, her face
did the thing it did in my dream,
the unwearing
back two years.
She pulled us into her arms
the way she used to.
We stood there, hugging and crying.
We soaked one another in
until the Littles got home.
And once again emotions
in the apartment
had to be quelled in order to keep others in the dark.

We ate pizza, delivered.
We did our homework to music
while Mom cleaned the house.
We all went to her at least once

with questions about our homework.
I wonder how many of my sisters made their questions
up,
knew the answer but went to her anyway,
like I did?

INHERITANCE

There was no punishment
for skipping school to visit Liam.
Instead, Mom held us like before,
as constricting as a tourniquet.
If she let us go again,
we might have all bled out.

She saw us for the first time
since Daddy was no more
and we no longer had the house
and we had to leave our schools.
And she loved us still
as much as she had before
when she saw us
again.

She wasn't around more,
But when she was present again,
little things like pats on our bottoms
and gentle nose pinches resumed.
Spontaneous dance sessions were revived.

We had existed in a state of stunted growth.
Now, the Littles lengthened six inches each with glee.

I remained stagnant.
Not ready to expand fully,
afraid of being punctured,

deflated, laid flat
again.
Afraid of bleeding out.

Freesia filled herself with something else,
a volatile mix of hope and confusion
on the verge of bursting.

The evening, Liam's mom showed up at our door,
the apartment diffused with
bitterness, glee, hope, caution, rediscovery.
A confused concoction
ready to implode
or to wrap us up
in one accord.

The bell rang,
interrupting our inner sanctum,
as the Littles helped Mom
cook dinner
and I helped Freesia and Zinnia
with their science fair project—
Varying Levels of Lead in Our City Water.

They were compiling months of research.
They had forced Liam to bring water samples from his
house
and his school.
We'd smuggled samples out of the library and, later,
the hospital.

Mom walked to the door, rubbing damp hands
on the old checkered apron
Daddy bought her one Christmas

as an inside joke they'd refused to share.

I'm Sonya Glenn,
said Liam's mom to ours.
I wanted to come sooner, but…

All our chatter ceased as quickly as
someone snuffing out a candle at midnight.

I'm Liam's mother.
Your girls are Liam's closest friends.

I hadn't thanked God before
for making sure we were discovered,
but I thanked Him then.

For all of Mom's acceptance and forgiveness,
there would have been nothing worse for us
than if Mrs. Glenn unveiled our secret.
If a stranger at her door
had been Mom's source,
reporting our friendship with Liam,
the hospital visit would have come up.
And the full summer days.
The embarrassment alone
of this woman,
this stranger,

knowing more about us
than Mom…
Acceptance and forgiveness wouldn't have come without
punishment!

But now, primed,
Mom opened wide the door.

We're just in the middle of preparing dinner.
Please, come in.
Will you eat with us?

The two of them spoke more,
muffled
as they made their way
into our living room.

Zinnia, Freesia, and I
dropped the project
and focused every part of our bodies
on finishing dinner
with the Littles.
Except our ears,
which strained to
catch every audible word
Mom and Mrs. Glenn said.
They did way too much whispering.

I'm sure you know
that Liam and your girls were…
I don't know how I can describe

197

it. I didn't even know.
I found his journals—
an entire box.
At first, I thought it was beautifully written fiction;
Liam has always been an exceptional
writer. But it was his life.
A whole life
of his that I knew nothing about.

A sigh from Mom,
I have to tell you
I didn't know, either.
I had no idea until I caught
Freesia and Iris skipping school
to visit him.

A collective intake of breath,
impaling,
came from the four youngest Flowers.
Zinnia glared at me.
She would never dare to glare at Freesia.

Well, I hope they didn't get into too much trouble.
Your sweet girls got me through.
All of us. My husband. My mom.
They gave us a lifeline.
Honestly.
Somehow when I saw them
in person,
I felt like I was watching the movie
after reading the book.

198

Seeing them brought him back to life,
gave me hope.
And Liam…
Liam started responding.
He's doing better.
It had to be them.
His prognosis is promising.
I feel like a witness to a miracle,
like prayers I didn't know to pray
have been answered.
Because of your girls.

Her voice changed
when she mentioned us.
Faraway,
longing to be close.

Mom did not allow
the silence
to take off its coat.
I'm so pleased.
It's been a whirlwind
of rediscovery.
If I'd known, I might have
prevented their friendship.
No. I definitely would have.
I wouldn't have trusted him,
and I had no time to get to know him.
Your Liam sounds lovely.

He loves them.

A smile in Mrs. Glenn's voice.
And it's clear they love him,
even if he is just a white boy.
A wink in her tone.

She swiveled her head then
to look at us,
her smile
lighthearted.
I tried to make myself a mirror,
but my return was heavy-hearted.

Freesia looked down at her feet,
and tears sprinkled her fuzzy socks.
Amaryllis and Dahlia
stood on the verge of crying.

Which brings me to why I'm here…
Liam's mother paused, tentatively promising,
but Mom, not ready to hear,
interrupted,
Girls, how's dinner coming?

Zinnia replied,
Sizzling and Set,
which is a family thing.
Freesia's groan remained in the kitchen.

There was no discussion about Mrs. Glenn
eating with us.
It was simply understood.

Mom rose from the couch,
and we fell into our mealtime routine,
every girl on her job—
a tablecloth of burnt orange, chocolate, turquoise and ivory
flapped sharply into place,
a matching runner rolled out like red carpet,
perfectly down the center.
Serving bowls and spoons
lined single-file down the lacy fabric.
Dishes clattered into place,
with napkins cushioning utensils.
A plastic pitcher of sweet tea,
made special when Mrs. Glenn showed up.
Brownie batter poured into a glass pan
and slipped into the oven
just before we all took a seat,
gave thanks,
and began to eat.

We did not go around
listing the highs and lows of our day.
No one complained of being kicked under the table.
Dahlia did not smack or chew with her mouth open
or talk with her mouth full.
We girls hardly talked at all.

Instead, we viewed Mrs. Glenn
through our periphery
as she ate,

wiped her mouth,
murmured about how tasty everything was.
She and Mom looked eye-to-eye,
chatted about weather,
work, recipes, church, schools,
books.
Daddy and Liam were mentioned in almost-whispers.
They sat with us, invisible,
squeezed in
at an overflowing table made for six.

A silence settled after the small talk exhausted.
Mom's shoulders resigned to the unknown
that she could put off
no longer.

Mrs. Glenn set her spine,
bent on her message and
braced
for Mom's reaction.

Phillip and I have a foundation.
We support many bright children
internationally
with funds to help them further their educations.
We've never supported anyone here
in the States.
We want to now.
We want to send your Flowers
to Brookside Academy.

Her voice was all business,
like a news anchor in monotone.
If it wasn't for the catch that rested there
that matched the snag in Mom's eyes,
I wouldn't have recognize her at all,
not as the woman at the hospital.
I couldn't tell from looking
into Mom's eyes
whether she was offended
by the stranger calling us by
the nickname Daddy trademarked
or by the offer of money,
thrown at us like charity.

Of course, we wouldn't be paying
full tuition for any of them.
It's all worked out with the school,
who quite frankly have not kept
their end of the bargain with respect to scholarships.
Your girls would attend at a significant discount.

Mom spoke hesitantly,
Even with the discount,
that school costs forty thousand dollars a year.
I don't see how we could accept such a…

Mrs. Glenn cut her off.

We didn't know
Liam was plagued by our privilege.
Philip and I gave him a mission:

Make the change you want to see in the world.
But we sent him out unarmed.

He was withdrawn
He acted resentful.
I waved him off.
"Typical teen,"
I scoffed.
"Such an attitude of entitlement."
I blamed us, his parents, for spoiling him.

And then I went right back to helping
everyone else's kid
while my son dug himself a hole of anguish
and jumped in.

Here her voice reverted back to
the breadth
it had with us in the hospital
and the small talk with Mom.
The warm maple syrup.

I wondered
which voice she used with Liam before he jumped.
I knew which one she would use ever after.

His therapist believes Liam needs to feel empowered to make an
impact on the world.
Liam wrote over and over
that he doesn't belong at Brookside Academy
but your Flowers do.

Let us send them there.

Mom stopped chewing,
placed her fork on the table,
stared at a blank spot on the wall
above Mrs. Glenn's head.

We absolutely accept your offer.

Azalea blinked rapidly,
willing herself to wake from a dream.
Dahlia's hands collided;
one resounding, elated clap.
Then her hands froze and she scanned our faces,
as if waiting for the punchline.
Amie swallowed her milk audibly.
Zinnia rubbed her hands along her thighs.

Freesia's eyes shone like the dollar coins
Daddy used to pull from our ears
like magic.

Mom made us return trinkets
given to us by generous friends in school—
erasers shaped like kitten faces,
plastic bracelets,
faded and torn pencil pouches,
toys they had in duplicate, triplicate—
ever conscious that we not be perceived as sponges.

You're here, Sonya,

205

strong and straight.

Liam's mom opened her mouth,
shook her head.
But Mom stopped any words she contemplated.

Really! That's the word that came to me
when I took you in at the front door —
Straight as an arrow.
You nearly lost your son.
Your only child
lies in pieces in a hospital bed,
and you have the courage to leave him
to offer blessings on us,
full-bodied,
intact.
If I asked you now how often you've left him lying there in that
hospital bed,
I know what your answer would be.
I know you sleep there,
shower there,
eat the hospital food.
And yet, here you are.

My Flowers are important to you.

I've been wallowing in self-pity
for two years.
I bottled up my grief and
I've been spraying it on daily.
Here you are, transforming yours

into something useful.

Mom was crying.
Liam's mom was crying.

They stood and embraced,
experimental and rigid at first,
but then they melded into one another
heart to heart,
which reminded me of Ma Moore.

We Flowers whooped,
danced and jumped.
But, there was a tinge,
a prickling within my happy.
Like almonds—
loving the taste of them,
but hating how they wax rubbery against my teeth.

When God finally let the Children of Israel
enter the promised land, they went without Moses.
When Mom said we could go to Brookside,
I knew Ma Moore would be our Third.

Even after Mrs. Glenn's offers
to help clean up were shot down,
all of the brownies were eaten
or sent home to Mr. Glenn,
the dishes were handled,
baths were taken,
and beds climbed into,

we stayed awake,
wondering what exactly Liam could have written
about us
that made his parents willing to spend
hundreds of thousands
of dollars on our education.

Mom had patiently
deferred our questions,
claiming to be too exhausted
to even think.
But I know her face
as well as I know her heart;
thinking was all Mom would do.

HOMECOMING

I had only ever been called
to the principal's office for accolades
or as a witness to some incident.
But when I was paged the first school day of spring,
I couldn't help but think of Freesia
and me skipping school.
What if they'd found out?

On my walk to the front office,
I envisioned the school having secret agents
who were notified when we were absent
and sent to check up on us,
to make sure we were legit.
I imagined the school paying for agent salaries
instead of decent books,
desks that don't eject
splinters like porcupines,
carpet that doesn't smell like leaky roofs,
neglected,
paint that isn't the color of the end of throwing up
when there's nothing left but bile.

I imagined two agents in slightly shimmering suits,
dark grey and navy blue,

dressed better than Freesia and me,

following us to Liam's hospital bed,

standing in the shadows
where we'd tried to hide,
those curly, cloudy-clear thingies
in their ears,
reporting back to Mrs. Fields.
I would maintain the lie, of course,
because Mom already knew.
I wouldn't get into trouble at home.
I'd say I was sick at home,
had permission to stay.
I'd forgotten to bring the note she'd written
excusing me.

But when I got to the front office,
Mom was sitting there.
My knees buckled.
It had been weeks since I'd thought
of the third death.
Now it stabbed me in the heart.

Mom's back was to the glass wall
that showcased the front office.
She turned to see me.
She didn't quite smile,
but she wasn't frowning.
No one had died.
My knees fortified.
She walked out of the office
before I even got to the door.

I need to take you somewhere.

She looked like a nervous daughter,
asking permission
of her mother.
I had no experience being a mother.
I nodded,
nervous, too.

We walked outside together,
and she reached for my hand.
We inched toward the bus stop like that—
her holding onto me like a probing cane,
me with no idea where we were going.

We passed the stop,
but it didn't register for me that we were in the parking
lot
until we were.
I hadn't seen Mom's van in nearly two years.
Suddenly, there it was before us,
gleaming in the sun—

life rewound.

We weren't holding hands anymore,
so she used one hand to grab her purse
and the other to pull out her keys.
It was the old keyring
with keychains from beach vacations
and a trip to Disney
and a pompom keychain Azalea
insisted she buy at a craft show.

Daddy always said Mom bought big purses
just to accommodate her keyring.

I heard the car mechanism unlock
and grabbed the handle
to open the door on my side.
If I didn't allow the questions to swirl around
in my head, I could almost pretend
two years hadn't happened.

But Mom was still sullen
and quiet and skinny.
So I had to not see her,
not even see her out of the corner
of my eye
to make myself rewind.

I closed my eyes and leaned my head back.
The van still smelled like rotten strawberries.
We had all tried to tell Mom the air freshener she picked
was awful,
but she loved it and it was her car.

If Mom still had her car,
I wondered if she still had Daddy's, too.

I'm so sorry. Iris,
she said, as if in answer
to my unasked question.
She put the van in reverse
and backed out of the parking spot.

I kept my eyes closed for many
stops and turns.
And Mom didn't say anything else.
She didn't even turn on music.

Usually in the car,
in the old days,
Mom kept the music on so low
I wondered, what was the point
of playing it?
Daddy played the music in his car so loudly
that sometimes the bass
would give us extra heartbeats,
make our teeth feel shaken loose.
If Mom was driving, he'd complain
about not being able to hear the music.

Because your eardrums are shot
from playing your music so loud.
We can all hear the music perfectly fine,
right girls?

We all knew not to get in the middle
of their disagreements.

One afternoon, we came across
ballroom dancers in the park —
a very old couple,
dressed in formal wear,
looking like they didn't belong

213

in a park full of families and kids
climbing and swinging,
sliding and running.
Mom and Daddy were like that—
sometimes they were in a different dimension
from the rest of the world.
They danced around one another,
perfectly in sync—

their steps
mesmerizing,
cadence
captivating
the perfect duo.

Even when arguing.

Things that were fixed in my life before,
things that had been broken for so long,
came back.
The way Mom used to sing so perfectly,
taking on the style and key of any singer on the radio.
Daddy bobbing his head to the beat of the music,
closing his eyes while he drove,
fluttering my heart with the thrill of his risk.
Something Mom never would have done.

Risk.

In the silence,
Mom breathed.

And I breathed.
And when I opened my eyes,
we were in our old neighborhood,
two streets from our street.
One minute from our house.

I really believed I was imagining it,
but when I finally allowed myself
to look at her,
I saw.
She had lied to us.

Mom parked in our driveway.
I jumped out and slammed the door,
not giving her the chance to try to stop me.
I rushed to the gate and jiggled
it the way you could to make it open
even if it was locked on the other side.
It opened with a squeak
that Daddy would have silenced with lubricant.
I ran to the back, all the way
to Daddy's garden.

Only when I was there,
inhaling the bouquet,
did I hear Mom close the driver's side door.
I heard her feet connect with the stone path
that led from the gate to the garden.

I wanted her to stay in the car.
I wanted her to drive away.

I didn't want to smell her hair pomade,
see her face,
hear the truth.

It thrived without him.
Mom sounded disappointed.
Because his touch,
his love
was an everlasting,
time-released
fertilizer,
securing their survival.
He had that way with you girls, too.
You have all surprised me
with your flourishing.
and shamed me
with my shriveling.
I forgot everything he planted inside me.
But I'm back, Iris.
I'm here now.
My mother stood behind me.

I didn't have to face her
to know
the tears that slid down her cheeks
were thick.
I could hear them
in the cracks of her throat,
in her stillness.
They matched my own,
heavy,

loud.
Like exhausted,
lead-footed legs.

Her arms made a bridge
from her body to my shoulders.
Disconnected.
Wrapped around my waist.
Embraced
as she put her chin on
my shoulder.

Daddy told you girls everything.
He was bigger than any bad thing that could ever happen.
But he didn't tell you my story
because it was mine
and I didn't want to remember.
I had a family.
I had people.
But I grew up in public housing, Iris,
and I shivered alone under that thundering cloud
until Daddy raised an umbrella over my head.
and led me to a different way of life.

He insisted I tell him everything.
Halting,
reticent,
the past formed words.
The words left my lips.
His passion for me
evaporated my past into thin air.

217

In the sunshine of our love,
he never saw my past,
but it hovered over me,
quiet,
mostly forgotten,
until he was gone.
Then, everything rained down,
acidic.
My mother's hacking cough,
her spittle as she barked,
"You'll be back."

I felt her sigh against my neck,
but my breath was held in check.
As much as we knew about Daddy's childhood,
we knew nothing about Mom's.

When Daddy died, I was lost
and ran to what I knew.
But I never sold the house.
It has always been ours.
We can go back.

But, I need your help.

Adults aren't supposed to ask kids for help.

For one heart-exalting millisecond,
I thought what I had so many times
right after:
Maybe Daddy was just a temporary awful.

Maybe all of this was a mixed-up nightmare.

Of course not.
That lie would be indefensible.

With the rent I charged
the family who lived in our house—our home with Daddy—
I didn't have to pay the mortgage here
or the rent on our apartment.

I knew Mom would want
me to make this right
with my sisters,
especially Freesia.

She'd want me to hustle her story
to them all.
They aren't stupid,
but Zinnia, Amie, and Dahlia
would be easy.
They still thought fairy tales were real and every story
ended
in happily-ever-after.
They'd eagerly devour
any version of Mom's story I chose to weave
for their naive benefit
and for the benefit of Mom.
Azalea would see right through me
to my truth,
which was not Mom's.
My truth made Mom a deceiver

219

and two years of our lives
a cruel hoax,
an unethical experiment.

No one could con Freesia,
except maybe Daddy.
But Daddy never needed to.

Freesia would say Mom played the part
of scheming scientist,
injecting a toxic lie,
into us;
uninformed
Tuskegee Airmen,
gullibly offering
ourselves up for multi-generational disease.
The worst part of the lie—
that Daddy had failed to provide for us—
had been omnipresent and
unspoken.

How could Mom expect me to
quell Freesia's righteous fury?

Mom wasn't afraid of her.
Mom was never that kind of mom,
but she was ready for the pain to go away.
She wanted to bypass the confusion, anger, and disbelief.
She wanted to skip ahead to the happily-ever-after.

I wanted happily-ever-after, too,

but our happily-ever-after died with Daddy.
I knew I wouldn't feel it again
until we had the certainty of the
third death.

I tried to use the van,
but I kept hearing Daddy laugh at me—
about my slow driving
about my too quiet music
about my air freshener.
One day, I just walked right past it.
I took the bus.
I felt free from the memory of him,
insufficient and gnawing,
at least for the walk and the bus ride.
So, I kept the van parked.

I've been parked, too.
Without the memories,
I have nothing left of him
except the six of you.
I've idled here long enough.
If I don't drive on,
I deliver the misconception
that you are not enough,
and you'll all leave me behind
the way I left my own mother behind.
We will be okay, Iris.

I remembered then,
that Ma Moore said the biggest human burden

and fallacy
is to think we have control,
that life is all up to us.
We play God and feel so much pressure.
There is relief in trusting that He
has the ultimate say.

I couldn't blame Mom
for relying on herself,
for moving us,
deserting us,
withering.
Mom didn't know God.

Why do you send us to church
when you don't even believe in God
yourself?

I knew they would reinforce our core values,
watch over you.
They were less likely
than the rest of the world
to harm you.
I knew you would be safe there.
Or safer there than anywhere else.

I channeled Freesia.
Safer, even, than being with you.
Plus, it was free,
I added,
more revelation

than accusation.

I must have said it in my head, though;
Mom didn't even flinch.

On our way back to the apartment,
We didn't talk.
I knew Mom had shared all she could.
Her story would have to come out in scattered showers.

Joiya Morrison-Efemini

AUTOBIOGRAPHY

Later, after dinner
and cleanup
and showers,
Mom piled us all in the car and drove us back home,
in our PJ's and with minty, smooth teeth.

Out of the car,
we all took the same route as earlier—
around to the side of the house,
through the fence
to the garden.
A few moments of silence
and then Mom ushered us onto the deck.

We stood behind her as she used her key
to unlock the French doors,
new since we left home
to replace the sliding glass door that would always
be a symbol of Daddy's death;
a stigma the picnic table and grill had inexplicably
escaped.

Through the French doors,
we sat on the carpet of the empty sunroom,
cross-legged
or legs straight out
or folded off to the side.

224

Girls, I didn't sell the house.
I rented it out to cover the mortgage
and the rent on our apartment.
We have Daddy's life insurance, too,
every cent unspent and earning interest.
I wasn't sure it would be enough
to have the same life,
and I couldn't bear that same life, anyway.
Not without him.

Freesia's eyes narrowed to poisoned darts,
and I turned away before her fire
infected me.
Mom didn't look at her.
Mom didn't look at anyone.
Except me.

I didn't know
how to subsist on a profit from his death.
He had provided a way for us.
In death, he offered us the chance to live
as if he were alive.
That felt like a curse to me.

Slowly, one by one,
my sisters understood that we could have stayed home,
tended the garden,
walked the dog,
kept the dog,
and said *goodbye* to him.
Played the piano,

225

kept our friends,
our schools,
our teams.

I couldn't think about
how to afford all the things:
food
clothes
utilities
activities
the car he wanted you to have at sixteen
and the gas to drive it
college.

I literally could not
add or subtract.
I'd sit at the kitchen table,
ready to set a budget,
and I'd see him
sitting across from me.
Always frowning.
Your Daddy never frowned at me.
I couldn't think.
Especially here.
He was everywhere.
But in that apartment, it's worse.
He's nowhere.

The Littles jumped up,
danced,
gurgled like full-bellied infants.

All they heard was that we could move back home.
We could go back to our regular life,
still incomplete, but home.

Freesia's gaze remained deathly.
She couldn't dislodge the bullet.
We could have stayed.
We should have stayed.

Mom had packed cleaning supplies
in the van
and the vacuum.
We unpacked it all.
We'd be back bright and early
the next morning to get the house spic and span.

Freesia stayed away,
cleaning wherever Mom and I were not.
There was a minute when we three were together
with no Littles,
and Mom said,
My mother told me once
that I was meant to live in public housing
and could never escape it.
When Daddy died,
for the first time
since I decided he would be my life partner, her voice was louder
than his.
I ran back out of fear
and guilt.

I don't have to tell you girls,
do I?
Not to let fear or guilt
chart your course?
I don't have to tell you
because you're Daddy's Flowers.

It was the first time she'd called us Flowers since Daddy
died.

We would all be happy to be back home.
Dahlia would sing and dance at the top of her lungs
with no neighbors to bang on their paper-thin walls and
ceilings
to rattle our walls and floor.
Zinnia and Amaryllis would go back
to their friends and their teams.
Freesia, too, eventually
would grow weary of wearing bitterness.
She would fall back in,
weighted and wavering,
but in.
It was Mom I wondered about.
Would she keep her armor on?
Would she meld into us?

Immediately,
contract negotiations began.
Trust in Mom had sunk into an abyss of

Reserve.

My sisters wanted something set
in stone.
I knew it was as futile as
The Commandments from God.
The Israelites couldn't keep them,
even with miracles happening daily.

A seven-item list was created:

Mom would never again lie to us. (Freesia)
She promised to keep the house and us in it forever.
(Dahlia)
She would be home with us for dinner at least three days
a week. (Azalea)
She would do the Littles' hair. (Amaryllis)
She'd allow at least one extra-curricular activity per
Flower. (Zinnia)
She would start going to church with us every Sunday.
(Me)

And the seventh thing,
because our beloved cocker spaniel, Copper,
had passed away at fourteen
in the care of one of Daddy's former work buddies
without us to comfort him:

We would get another dog. (All the Littles)

Moving out of the house
had been all sniffles

and stomped feet,
mindless bickering,
and pouted lips.

Moving back in was not the opposite.
We still bickered mindlessly, but the stomping
was a rebranding,
as if we could imprint our feet into the floors
so that ours would be the only steps to ever comfortably
tread the carpet and tile and hardwoods.
So that no one would ever dare try walking long-term
where we were embedded permanently.
We marked our territory for future squatters
resentfully,
as if the tenants instead of Mom had pushed us out.

We cried joyful tears when Dahlia screamed from the
basement
that our height markings,
sketched in pencil religiously
twice a year by Daddy
in the little storage cubby
under the stairs
had not been erased.

We released fretful sighs
over mementos
painted over,
broken,
fixed,
or disappeared entirely.

There had always been six floating shelves
in the family room
that bore our current year's school picture.
Now one was slanted and another chipped.
Gone was the delicate silver hummingbird
wind chime that we could always see
spinning and swaying, but never hear
except at night
when the world fell asleep
and only in the back bedrooms
once the sounds of us living life dozed off.

The mural that Dahlia had drawn
when she was two
in permanent marker
along the side of the kitchen cabinets
as Mom cooked dinner, unaware,
had been painted over.

Mom had screamed when she'd seen it
and lamented to Daddy as soon as he walked through the
door from work.
Ahhhh!
He'd exclaimed, smiling.
My little Picasso!
He plucked Dahlia up off the floor and held
her like a bouquet in his arms.
That mural was meant to be there to annoy Mom forever.

We spent all of June

231

making home again.
We bought a large butterfly wind chime loud enough
to be heard
over our sniffling, bickering, and stomping.
Freesia installed six new floating shelves
that she'd bought second-hand
and painted
red, purple, orange, yellow, blue, and green.
She'd found six small flower pots
in the basement
and ordered each of us to paint one.
We all decided to design our pots with the flowers
we were named after.
Once they dried, she placed one on each shelf.

The end result was akin to Daddy's garden,
something an outsider would observe as beautiful
without the capability to comprehend
the scope.
It was us planting our roots
in that house,
a network that would flow from those pots
into the walls and create a system throughout
as ordinary
and fundamental
as the house's electrical wiring
and plumbing.

Mom had put most of our
things into storage
or the basement

or the attic,
and everything we had in the apartment
was no longer taken for granted,
suddenly what we needed
instead of all we had in the world.

All the second-hand trinkets
and steals of deals
mixed in with everything from before
was just enough to make it almost
the house we'd had with Daddy,
different enough to be a familiar place
from which we could forge ahead.

It took us several weeks to move back home.
In those weeks,
droplets of the life Mom led
before
precipitated into images
that drizzled from her lips
into our minds
finally.

She walked by and saw me fussing with my hair in the
mirror.
My mother did hair from our apartment.

You have her stylistic creativity, Iris.
She wasn't looking at me, but at a spot on the wall above
my head.

When the Littles poured over the wedding album,
which had been painstakingly wrapped and
securely hidden away in the attic
with some other sentimentalities,
My mother and father were never married,
Dad only lived with us off and on,
between other girlfriends
and other children.

Catching us mid-bicker, she'd admonish,
You should treasure your sisters.
I don't have a sister.
Just three brothers by my father,
none of whom I know.
I always wanted a sister.

To Freesia,
who went weeks without speaking to either of us,
You remind me so much of my mother, Free.
Your grandmother was beautiful—
tall and thin,
with milky, caramel skin.
She had long nails that she always kept painted
in bright colors.
It's funny how genes can give you the mannerisms of a person
you've never met.
You move your hands just like she did.

Once, when Liam's mom came to sleep in our guest room
because Liam and his dad had gone fishing,
she and Mom sat in the living room,

covered in fleece blankets,
sharing a bottle of champagne
and talking until way past midnight.

I overheard Mom tell Mrs. Glenn,
Most women have girlfriends.
I never needed one.
I never trusted one.
My mother had my Aunt Lucille.
She was my dad's sister, so Mother never had to worry
about her stealing my Dad.

She never told me not to trust other women,
but I think I learned it anyway.

Aunt Lucille cooked all our meals.
In exchange, Mother did her hair
whenever she wanted.

Our place was always full of women —
cackling and cussing,
drinking and, once or twice, fighting,
usually over men.
But Mom didn't tolerate the fights.
She'd put them out.
Mom always had a cigarette in her hand or close by in an
ashtray.
After five o'clock, she'd pour herself a rum and cola over ice
and nurse it for the rest of the night.
If Dad was home, he'd pour her drink and hand it to her
at five o'clock sharp

235

without being asked.

Amaryllis caught me spying then
and asked,
Whatcha doin'? so loudly
that I had to shush her silently,
grab her by the arm,
and usher her back upstairs.
I missed whatever else Mom might have revealed.

Everything we did or said seemed to take Mom
backwards.
Sometimes she'd dish,
and other times she'd just stare off
with a half-smile
and eyes half full of tears.

When report cards came, Mom doled out
a crisp twenty-dollar bill
to each of us
for the first time since Daddy died.

My mother didn't care how I did in school.
She wanted to make sure I knew how to do hair.
I had no desire to have my fingers in people's scalps all day.
She said I thought I was better than her,
that I didn't appreciate what she did to keep me clothed and fed.
She said women would always have hair.
No one who could do hair would starve.
She wanted security for me.
She only knew of one way,

236

so that was all she had to teach.

But, Dad?
He wanted me to go to college.
He regretted dropping out of high school.
He felt constricted by the cage
his limited education had engineered.
He was never harsh with me unless I brought home grades he thought were
beneath my potential.
At first, I tried hard in school to please him.
Then teachers started to treat me differently.
I got awards.
They gave me books, free passes to museums,
expensive pens and notebooks
behind the backs
of the other students.
These days people would wonder about the motives
of a teacher like that,
but I was lucky;
they just wanted me to succeed.
I soaked it all up.
I earned awards.
I won the spelling and geography bees.
My standardized test scores were so impressive,
I skipped a grade.

She turned to Amaryllis—
See, all your smarts didn't come from Daddy—
and winked.

When the twenty dollars burned holes in everyone's
pocket
except Zinnia's,
Mom told us,
My Dad started saving money for me to go to college.
He opened a bank account that only he had access to.
My mother hated that bank account.
She wanted access to the money.

I couldn't understand why Mother was so obsessed with
that money.

Dad had never provided for Mother and me.
His money went to his other kids
and women.
Mother made enough money for us.

Every once in a while Dad would tell me
how much money was in the account —
sneak into my room and whisper it to me at night
or dance me around the room and shout it if Mom was out.
One thousand dollars.
Five thousand dollars.
Seven thousand dollars.
I felt like a millionaire.
I didn't know anyone who had that kind of money
just sitting, waiting for them.
He taught me that it's okay to use your money,
but it's better to save it.
Have a goal and put money away toward it.
When daddies are gone,

what they've taught you doesn't have to disappear.
You can keep it.

Mom's words floated through the house
like the perfumed dance of a scented candle,
her memories leaving faint remnants
of events she'd previously tried to
mask—
Daddy's cologne,
little girls' strawberry lip gloss,
the fancy soaps Azalea coveted,
dryer sheets,
cedar chests,
home-cooked meals,
and the musk of adolescence.
All of Mom
finally cemented
with all of us,
rebuilding
a more robust foundation.

It was Dahlia who asked,
either brave enough despite
what we all expected
or naïve enough
that she didn't suspect a thing.

How did your parents die?

A heavy breath.
A microscopic tear,

239

only perceivable
after the wipe of her cheek
by the satiny streak left behind.

One afternoon while I was in school,
a woman Dad had left for Mom—again—
came to the apartment under the guise of getting her hair done.

Aunt Lucille told me all the details—
she'd dropped by to give Mom a week of meals.
The woman was in the chair, and she and Mom were talking
and laughing.
Then Dad came in.
He recognized the woman and asked her what she was doing
there,
only not so nicely.

She stood and pulled a gun from her purse.
Shot my Dad in the head,
point blank.
Once,
and he was gone.

I was eleven.

She shot Mom three times.
Leg.
Arm.
Shoulder.

Aunt Lucille wrestled the woman,

stabbed her with a kitchen knife,
made her drop the gun.

Mom was in the hospital for weeks.
I stayed with Aunt Lucille.
We got evicted because Mom had been running a business
out of her apartment.

Aunt Lucille said it was just an excuse.
Everyone knew Mom ran that business out of our apartment.
She'd been doing it for ten years.

We weren't eligible for any other public housing
because we'd been evicted from one.
Mom had to rent an apartment.
She had to pay the full rent herself.
She continued to do hair when she could,
but she had a lot of pain in her right hand from the bullet that
hit her arm.
And she had a lot of anxiety whenever someone new came in.
Sometimes she sent them away.
Some days all she did was sleep.
She stopped waiting until five o'clock to drink her rum and cola.
And she never stopped at just one.

Aunt Lucille still brought us meals sometimes,
but we'd moved so far away that
she couldn't just pop by anymore.
She had a husband and kids of her own.
So I learned how to cook.

The summer I turned fourteen,
I took a lifeguarding and CPR course.
After that, I always had a job,
lifeguard,
babysitter,
cashier.
I gave all my paychecks to Mom.
We'd agreed that she'd keep one-third,
and the other two-thirds would go to my college fund.

I remained an honor student.
My counselor helped me apply to colleges.
She was sure I'd get scholarships,
and I did.
Mom fought tooth and nail to keep me home.
She said she needed me.
She said college was a waste of time.
But I would not be deterred.
My Dad was dead,
and I knew he'd wanted me
to go to college,
to do well,
to get a great job.
To succeed.

I would not be caged.

I went and I worked and I studied.
I was only a few hours away,

My mother seemed to hate me.

She never called me.
She rushed off the phone when I called her.
She spent most of my visits complaining.
Eventually, I only visited for the holidays
and just for a day or two.

My mother stopped,
as if the scent of memory had wafted out the window
and beyond her reach.
That was all she could give.
And we were grateful for it.

There was not a weekend that went by that
we didn't hang out with Liam's family.
By then, they were Auntie Sonya and Uncle Philip.
On Mom's first birthday back in the house,
we invited them over for dinner.
We ate fish tacos with homemade salsa.
Mom made margarita mocktails.
We had tres leches cake with dulce de leche ice cream for
dessert.

We played Ultimate Elimination,
a card game the Littles made up.
It was down to just Freesia and Liam.
Liam won.
But you still can't beat me in Spelling Smash.

Later, when it was just us again,
PJ's and slippers on,
fireplace glowing with embers

from the fire Uncle Philip and Azalea started,
Dahlia asked Mom how she and Daddy met.
Mom, who was always unsealed
and breezy after an evening with Aunt Sonya,
smiled bravely.

Second year, first semester,
I met your Daddy.
I had vowed I would not date
until my senior year.
I was so afraid of losing focus,
so afraid of forfeiting my scholarship.
I needed my college savings for grad school.

But your Daddy wooed me relentlessly.
It didn't help that he was tall and dreamy.
I agreed to one date.
I told him there would be just one.
Who was I kidding?
Not him!
But he played it so smooth.
He organized a picnic,
and then he told me
that even though he knew it would make him look cheap
to not spend money actually taking me out
to dinner or a movie,
he was just being smart;
since it was to be our one and only date,
he wanted to maximize getting to know me.
He wanted to know everything.
Plus, he admitted, he wasn't cheap;

244

he was broke.

Here, she laughed out loud.
A bit of her old self shone through the crinkle of her eyes.

He made me laugh.
From then on, it was your Daddy and me—
studying, talking, laughing, eating together.

He reminded me of my dad—
the way he could strike up conversation
and find common ground
with just about anyone—
but he was different with me than my dad
was with Mom.

My Dad was jovial and fun with everyone.
He was carefree with his love.
He could not be tied down.

Your Daddy formed this second skin
around the two of us.
It was invisible, but everyone knew
it was there.
He liked other people.
A lot.
But your Daddy loved me and only me.
And then, he loved all of you,
too.

I took Daddy to meet Mother.

She hated him.
She said he was too high on himself.
I think she hated him because he was high on me.

Your Daddy told me to give her time.

We got up early one Saturday
and drove three hours to the house your Daddy was raised in.
He was an orphan.
And not just because his parents had died.
Everyone who had loved your Daddy had died
or moved far away —
aunts, uncles, cousins.

Someone else owned the property.
But even just parking on the street,
getting out and standing there,
I could feel the love.
I could envision the cookouts,
birthday parties and Christmases
he'd told me about.

He got down on one knee right there
and proposed to me
in front of the memories of his childhood.
He gave me the ring his father
proposed to his mother with.
I've never taken it off.

He was a senior.
I was a junior.

We decided to get married the summer after my graduation.

Mom was against us, and I wanted to elope.
He thought I'd regret it.
And then,
so fast,
senior year.
He took a year off to work.
He had a really good engineering job.
We'd apply to graduate school together—
I'd get a Master of Education.
He'd get a Master of Engineering.

I got a full scholarship.
I called Mother to ask for my money.
We would have a small wedding.
We wanted to buy this little yellow house
in a cul-de-sac that we had found.
It was a fixer upper with boarded windows and dirt for a lawn.
But it was cheap and Daddy and I both were somewhat handy.
My dad had put at least $10,000 away for me.
I'd been sending my mom money from all my jobs.
I had trusted her with the deposits,
never asking questions.

But she said there was nothing left.
She hadn't saved my money.
She'd spent it all,
even the money Dad put away
She never apologized.

Your daddy drove me to her apartment that weekend.
I didn't talk to her.
I got everything that was mine—
everything I had paid for—
and I walked out.

I didn't know then that she had lung cancer,
that a lot of my money
had been used to pay for treatments
and then to make her more comfortable.
I didn't know then that she only had a few weeks left to live.

Honestly, I don't know if it would have made a difference to me
at the time.
Now...

Aunt Lucille called me to tell me that Mother was gone.
When she told me about Dad,
so many years before,
she had been tenderhearted.
She had consoled me.
We'd cried together.
When she called about Mother,
she was a different person.
She judged me harshly for abandoning Mother.

Here Mom began to cry.

Now I have you girls,
and I have failed you in so many ways.
Maybe I haven't made my Mother's specific mistakes,

248

but the choices we make can hurt our children.
I get it.
Even though we're supposed to be selfless,
sometimes moms are just people trying to survive,
in tatters.

Pregnancy interrupted my formal education
and ushered me into a new world of emotional intellect.
One by one,
Daddy and I arranged this exquisite bouquet.
I didn't want to spend even one second away.

Daddy's gone.
I tried to transplant us for a time,
doing my own brand of surviving in tatters,
but we are rooted here,
You are all blossoming.
It's time for me to blossom.
I finished my degree.
I'm going to work,
You're all going to Brookside,
and we will be okay.

Mom was still relying on herself.
She didn't know how to freefall into God.
With my sisters and Liam,
introducing them to God
felt natural.
With Mom, I needed Ma Moore.
I would ask her, the next time we saw her,
to witness to Mom.

The day after we unpacked the last box,
Ma Moore died in her sleep
before converting Mom,
before giving me my Bible verse,
and before I had forgiven
her for giving Freesia her verses
first.

Even the relief that we had our Death
Number Three
didn't numb the laceration
that slit my faith.

Ma Moore's Homegoing service
was nothing
like Daddy's funeral.

We went to Daddy's service devastated,
endured it like necessary surgery
without anesthesia.
We wished we could be dead right along with him.
We tried not to believe he was really
going to be six feet under by the end of the day.
We left even more devastated
when we thought that
more devastation was impossible.

We sent Ma Moore home to Jesus
with a party.
Sangin', clappin',

dancin'.
Telling stories about her
and laugh-crying.
We were alive,
blessed to have known her,
blessed to be in the presence
of others who loved her.
Blessed to have more days to carry on her legacy.
We knew exactly where she had gone.

By the time we buried Ma Moore,
we were happy for her.
We were assured
we would see her again
and she was with the One she loved
more than any of us.
She belonged
there with Him,
and we resolved
to do everything
to belong there with Him, too.

Ma Moore's was our third death.
I breathed fuller,
slept deeper,
walked lighter
after she died.
Liam was supposed to live,
so it was okay that Ma Moore didn't.
Except now I wouldn't get my verse.
I deserved to have my own verse more than anyone.

Definitely more than Freesia,
who didn't even love God.
I was the closest to Ma Moore.
Ma Moore left this world,
without giving me my verse
when I was the Flower keeping all the rest of them
prayed up.

LEGACY

Liam leapt in March.
Fractured both legs,
one elbow,
a cheekbone,
two fingers.
Cracked his skull.

God caught
him one-handed,
broke his five-story flight,
placed him more gently
than gravity would have.
Then God's hands healed him
completely.

By the end of
September,
he was back on the soccer pitch,
enchanting the ball
and beguiling
the rest of us
again.

He ditched his club team
and started playing for his new high school
because Uncle Phil finally cared more
about coaching philosophy
than team rank.

My dad really gets it,
and I'm loving soccer all
over again—
what it feels like to trust these guys
and have them trust me.
We're all supporting one another
and pushing one another.
We're winning
and losing together.

And the coach, Eye?

(Somewhere along the line, Liam had started calling me
"Eye,"
and I'd never even told him what Daddy had said
about me being a sentry, a keeper of light.)

Eye, the coach talks to the team as a whole.
He says we win and lose together.
He doesn't tolerate beef.
He's tough, and
he's smart
he's fair.

Liam continued therapy
and went to yoga
with a bunch of his soccer buddies
once a week.
They started on a dare
and then pretended they were only there

because the last one to quit
would get $10 from each of the rest of them.

Monday through Friday,
Mom dropped us off at Brookside Academy
in pleated plaid skirts and hunter grey tops
with burgundy embroidery.
Our van was not fancy.
Our shoes were not overpriced.
Yet
like everyone else,
we strode
through the massive gilded gate
toward double doors,
our backs to Brooks Street Housing,
and disappeared entirely
into a land of brand new books,
our refurbished laptops bundled
in wheeled backpacks.
The teachers really did sing and dance
when we earned good grades;—
often terribly, always humorously.
We found ourselves in a
third world
in which we did not belong.
And because we were once secure
and then not,
our family once intact
and then not,
our lives purposeless
and then not,

255

we were comfortable foreigners,
carrying in our broken-and-then-not hearts
passports for admittance
into three worlds in two years
and anywhere else life might take us.

There are benefits to economic

Endowment.
The levity of walking
through corridors
unfamiliar
and feeling unfettered
by expectation,
feet permanently afloat
in-between
where you came from
and where you are going.
The hallways
at Brookside Academy are too young
and too unbounded
for anyone to predict what we will become.
We are part of a grand experiment
like everyone else.

Freesia felt free there
for the first time since Daddy died
to vent her most cynical self
or divulge her vulnerabilities,
and both were met

with circumspect
inquisition.
She was dared daily
to change her mind.

No one looked at anyone sideways there.

We spoke and everyone listened,
even when they disagreed.
Voice gave way to power.
Conviction gave way to
reevaluation,
amendment.
Change was
optional;
growth was mandatory.

Brookside Academy
was a field trip we took together —
students, teachers, administration, parents.
We'd pass or fail as a collective.
Everyone was charged with
evolution.

The entire school was part of a movement,
hoping to become a standard.

We aimed,
intent on being recognized.
Our hair,
our skin,

our voices—
all more than
enough.
Our teachers called on us
to take the future into our hands
and to mold it into whatever we wanted that was
beneficial for society as a whole.

To them
our ideas held promise.

Mom left us there
and drove ten miles to work.
In the two years we had lived across the street,
she had earned her teaching certificate
so she could teach fourth grade gifted students
at a Title 1 school.

Liam's parents enrolled him in a less prestigious
charter high school,

Pathway to Impact.

He needed to feel that every miraculous
step he took
was propelling him toward changing the world
for the better.

He'll be a famous soccer star
and
end up founding a charity,

like his parents,
using his education,
his superstardom,
his influence
to send students to the schools they were meant
to attend all along.
He jumped in May,
but by God's mercy lived
and will learn to fly.

Saturdays were a blur of sports,
head starts on school projects,
housecleaning,
biking with friends,
gardening,
meal prepping for the week.

Liam came every Saturday
for family movie night.
Often Aunt Sonya and Uncle Phil
came, too.
To our moms,
Liam and I were a musical.
They watched,
rapturously sentimental, but also terrified
of our romance,
praying we would not fall into tragedy.

Freesia rolled her eyes and smirked.
Liam is just making his way through the garden.
Maybe when he goes after Dahlia,

Mom will finally throw him out.

But I knew a secret.
On our second visit to the hospital—
when Mom took all six of us
the day before Liam woke up—
the Littles had been too loud.
They made Liam forget his injuries
and get rowdy right along with them.
The staff had asked Auntie Sonya
(although back then she was still Mrs. Glenn)
if we could give Liam a chance to rest.
His heart rate and blood pressure soared, and that had
worried them.
We all ate lunch in the cafeteria,
and then Aunt Sonya and I went to the restroom
together.
You know, Iris,
It's always been you that Liam liked.
He flirted with Freesia because she was safe.
And, of course he loves you all.
But in his journals he goes on and on
about how beautiful and smart and kind you are,
how sometimes he can't breathe for the first few minutes
he's with you.
How he sees God when you show your heart.
His biggest regret was flirting with Freesia
because you were the one he'd wanted to flirt with
but didn't have the courage to.
And then it was too late to change course without looking like
an idiot,

and he knows you well enough to know you'd never date him,
thinking he liked Freesia first.
But I'm his mother.
Mothers are nosey and pushy and embarrassing.
So, I can tell you all of this despite how it might horrify him.
And it will horrify him when I tell him I told you.
But I will most certainly tell him.

Because horrified is magnificent.
Horrified means he's alive.

I stared at her in the restroom mirror.
Willing myself not to shriek,
not to jump up and down,
not to hug myself.
I hugged her placidly instead,
grateful for meddling mothers.

And, Iris, don't be so hard on your mom.
Mothers are nosey and pushy and embarrassing.
Despite our best efforts,
we're uncertain and fallible too.
Quite often, in fact.

We both came out of the restroom
with puffy red eyes
and silly smiles planted on our faces.

Sunday is still my favorite day.

We made the decision to

leave Grace Walk
by vote.
(I voted 'Nay.')
Now we all attended
Victory Bible Church—
Mom, us Flowers, Liam, Aunt Sonya and Uncle Phil.
Uncle Phil's brother Garyth started
joining us.
Sniffing around Mom,
Freesia remarked with no hint of emotion
either way.
We all sat by and watched Mom die.
Now that she was alive again,
there was nothing any of us would do
to entomb her.

Victory
was a modern church—
two simple buildings reminiscent
of a small-town elementary school.
Inside the main building
is a square
of hallways with classrooms on the outsides
and the worship center
in the center.

Victory
was multi-cultural and contemporary,
three come-as-you-are (jeans, cutoffs, tank tops) services,
two buildings,
worship center,

student center.

Ma Moore had brainwashed me.
In the beginning, it was hard to wear anything
but dresses and skirts.
Freesia had no problem at all.
She quoted the verse about God looking inside a person,
not outside.
I touted the scripture about making sacrifices
to make your brothers and sisters in Christ
feel comfortable.
Freesia retorted she didn't care about my comfort.
Ma Moore would have hated Victory.

Freesia, Liam, and I
attended services
in the Student Center,
complete with a cafe and
electronics charging station.

One Sunday, Freesia insisted on going to church early.
Mom had to drop her off,
and then come back home to ready herself
and organize the Littles.
Sunday breakfast was light
because we ate a big meal with the Glenns,
either Sunday lunch or dinner.

(Cookouts, restaurants, birthday celebrations—
we now had ten a year, eleven if we counted Uncle
Garyth.

More and more, we counted Uncle Garyth.)

Mom dropped me off at the Student Center
and continued on to find a parking space.
I walked into the building and then into
the auditorium.
The baptismal pool had been assembled up front,
which was strange.
Usually we were told when our peers
had made the decision to be baptized
and charged with praying for them.

We all sat down and the
screen lit up.
Personal testimonials
always played before baptisms.
Suddenly Mom, Aunt Sonya, Uncle Phillip
appeared
in the aisle.
I moved down, confused,
and they scooted into the chairs closest to mine.
I heard whispering and looked behind
me to find four of my sisters.

Liam's face lit up on screen,
and I instantly looked for Freesia.
She would not want to miss the opportunity
to find something during Liam's baptism
to tease him about.
But Freesia was nowhere.

Pre-recorded Liam sat for a moment,
just looking into the camera lens
and out at us.

This year has been really hard for me.
And also really easy.
I tried to take my own life
right after I accepted Jesus
because I didn't feel any different.
I thought I would feel
this enormous pressure to be perfect
lifted,
but I still felt the pressure to change the world,
to make it better.
I thought there would be this huge change.
Like I'd be perfect or something.
I felt I could never do enough
to be worthy of God.
But then God performed this miracle in my life.
He literally stopped me from dying.
I spent three weeks in a coma,
two months in the hospital.
He healed my brain,
my legs,
my arm,
my fingers,
my face,
my skull.
My doctors say I shouldn't be alive.
I shouldn't be walking.
I shouldn't have healed so fast

I shouldn't be able to play soccer.
God said that He could
to all of it.
I'll never be perfect.
I know now that I can make a difference in this world;
I'm supposed to take the good with the bad
and trust it will all end up exactly the way God wants it to.
I thank Iris, for teaching me this.
And Ma Moore for teaching her.
I thank God for saving me.
I want to show the world that I am committed to Him.

The screen went black.
The stage lights went on.
Liam was already in the pool
with his Uncle Garyth.
How did I miss that?
Liam was baptized in the name of the Father, Son, and
Holy Spirit.

The lights went out again, and
Freesia's face popped on screen.
In the moment before she spoke,
Mom tapped my shoulder.
Freesia has chosen you to baptize her.
Go to the back.

I rose in disbelief.
I walked,
her words drawing the disbelief out of me,

replacing it with tears of jubilation that could have filled the pool.
This is what I had prayed for more than anything—
Freesia to be saved.

I hated God
He took Daddy away,
or at the very least
He allowed him to be taken.
He let us lose our house.
Let us go to a poor neighborhood
and a poor school.
He let our Mom have to work two jobs
and go to school
and worry about us
and not be there for us.

Iris kept telling me how good He was.
I thought she was crazy.
Good people don't sit and watch
while other people suffer.
So how good could God be if that's what He did?
Either He was awful
or He didn't even exist.
But then I made a list of all the good things in my life
that came after Daddy died:

Ma Moore
Liam
My sister's faith
Stronger sisterhood

Grace Walk
Going to school with kids who were just like me on the inside,
where it matters
Living the way millions of people live
And learning not to take everything we have for granted.

I thought about what Iris told me—
that God's goodness
doesn't erase the bad;
it helps us survive the bad.
I looked at my sister,
who went through everything
with me, but didn't pummel
everything in her path
the way I did
and didn't resent
the way I did.
She loved.
She laughed.
She believed.
She hoped.
She cared.
She forgave.
I wanted what she had,
so I prayed a prayer
and I believed,
and my heart changed
little by little.
I looked for goodness,
and I saw goodness.
Now I want her to baptize

me to make a public statement
that I have joined His family.

I will have to always rely on Freesia's
account of her baptism.
The time between me walking to her
and the two of us heading to the back
to dry off
lives only in her memory,
but
I baptized my sister.

Months later, I would baptize Mom.

SECRETS IN THREES

My mouth curved into the same smile.
My throat replicated
a carbon-copy laugh.
I practiced in the mirror
to get them just right,
to hide the wound inside
that I could not define.
It stabbed every time I thought about
Freesia getting her verses first.
That she got verses.
I didn't even have one.

I could relate to what Liam said
about a heart refusing to follow a mind
made up.
I decided to forgive.
I was determined to be happy
about Freesia and Liam.
But I remained resentful.

Ma Moore died,
deferred me to last
and then ditched me.

I could unclench my heart
at the thought of never
being kissed by her,
hugged by her,

holding hands with her,
hearing her charmed ankles.

But never getting a verse from her?
Not even one?
My heart seized every time my mind remembered.

I felt like a hypocrite,
leading Freesia and Liam
to God
and telling them He was all they needed
and then holding a grudge so tightly.
Why?
Because I believed
Ma Moore was my intermediary to God?
Because she meant
more to me than God did?

No one noticed that I didn't read my Bible
anymore.
Ma Moore would call me a spiritual consumer
at Victory.
Ma Moore loathed spiritual consumerism.
She said it's as bad as atheism, maybe worse.
Atheists don't know any better and
Christians should.
I sat still on a stagnant relationship
with Him.
I decided what I believed and what I didn't
based on my feelings.
It's the opposite of what Ma Moore taught us—

271

to avoid being led into religious falsehood
by always reading the Bible and praying for
interpretation
for ourselves.

At Victory,
I didn't teach preschool.
I didn't teach anyone
anything
anymore.
There was no lesson to prepare.
Nothing forced me to go to my Bible.
I no longer yearned to read His words.
I didn't miss my conversations with God
at all.

But Freesia read her Bible every night.
At school she founded a club.

And then she encouraged her friends Avi
and Aara to found clubs, too,
so they could collaborate morning prayers
for students of all faiths.

They organized a bake sale fundraiser
for our sister school,

Chisolm Elementary,
and donated enough money for a cart full of laptops.
Selling brownies for two dollars helped,

but mostly Brookside Academy parents gave huge
monetary donations
in lieu of brownie purchases.
Freesia snickered that the moms couldn't go off their
diets,
even in the name of charity.
Only at Brookside.

If you were a student
at Brookside with an idea that advanced
the mission
of Brookside,
administration usually tried to make it happen.
Freesia, Avi, and Aara,
with their respective clubs,
promoted Brookside's charge
of tolerance,
cooperation,
respect,
equality.

We don't need believe exactly the same thing to make an impact,
to potentially change the world.
We were helped by Aunt Sonya and Uncle Phil
before they found Jesus.
Their son attempted suicide,
which led them to us.
Helping us led them to Him.
We don't know what's going on behind the scene with anyone's
salvation story.

Freesia smiled and winked at me.
And Jesus calls us to be light in the world.
I don't know about you, but I'm gonna shine my light
and let Jesus do the rest.

Her new-found faith and wisdom,
the prayer that had been steadily on my fervent list,
really ticked me off!

Because I couldn't not join Freesia's club,
I had to start reading the workbook
and participate in discussions
at least minimally,
which meant I had to read my Bible.
I opened it for the first time in months.
Stuck to the back flap was a bright purple envelope.
Literally stuck,
so that I had to pull it hard to detach it
and open it.
Inside was a letter
in Ma Moore's perfect script.

My Dearest Iris,

Girl, how long did it take you to find this letter? Never mind, I don't think I want to know! I'm sorry your Bible is ripped. But you'll always see that torn flap and have a story to tell. I couldn't think of any other way to make sure this note was not lost. It's important that you read it.

I wanted to talk to you in person, but with you all returning to your house, the school year ending, and all these ailments I've had lately,

I wasn't sure I'd get a chance and I wanted to be sure you would get your verse. I couldn't sleep well knowing I still had you to minister to.

I'm writing you now because I had an inkling. You know, when you just get a feeling you need to do something? I been getting a lot of them lately. Well, I told you before—I learned a long time ago to go ahead and follow that nudging. You never know where it might take you. And you never know where your obedience will take someone else.

I know sometimes you think your prayers go unanswered. Well, I'm here to tell you that they are not going unanswered. I told you before, God says OKAY or NOT YET or NOT QUITE LIKE THAT. Even His NO is an answered prayer. You just have to trust. That's all He requires.

If you stopped praying, start praying again. Even if all you say is WHY or PLEASE or HELP. I got to some low points in my life where all I could do was cry during prayer time. Sometimes all I could do was shake my head. HE knows your heart.

If you stopped reading your Bible, start again. Every day. You have the Word of the Most High God written out for you in your native tongue. Only a fool would ignore that. You, Iris, ain't nobody's fool!

Your heart is what I saw even before I was stunned by your beautiful brown eyes. Your heart is what people who are paying attention notice first. Iris, you are a woman after God's very own heart. Acts 13:22—But God removed Saul and replaced him with David, a man about whom God said, 'I have found David, son of Jesse, a man after my own heart. He will do everything I tell him to.'

Iris, you have a faith that is uncommon in your generation. Maybe it's uncommon in any generation. In all my years, I have seen none like you. You followed God when everything in your life pointed to Him being unloving or nonexistent. You were like the bleeding woman who had only heard about Jesus, and reached out to him for healing (Mark 5:24-29). Jesus himself says that those who have not seen but believed are blessed. You, Iris, are blessed.

You exemplify the fruit of the spirit (Galatians 5:22-23). You love your family and your friends unconditionally. You teach the preschool children with so much energy and so much joy. You are able to keep the peace even when your sisters try to stir you up. You persevere through all of the adversity your family has faced. You are kind and good and faithful. You gently raise those rascally Littles. And you exhibit self-control by not secreting away with that boy that you love so fiercely. Yeah, girl, I know you're smitten with that boy. Keep your integrity close to you. Always do what you know is right. You hear what is right as a whisper in your ear. I know you do.

See, now. You can sift through this letter and find three verses so far that all pertain to you. I have one more to give you. But I don't want you to go counting and comparing verses. Remember we are not to compare ourselves to others. Christianity is not a competition. This Bible verse gifting is not a competition, either. It's just Ma M following what God put on my heart. In your lifetime, you'll find innumerable verses that are fitting. Apply them all!

I want you to always remember David and how like him you are. I want you to be courageous as you battle things that seem so much bigger than you. They are not bigger than you because you are a child of the Most High God. He is for you so that nothing can prevail against you.

I love you so much and I am so honored to be your Ma M. Always.

Ma Moore's letter
was a call to soar
on wings like eagles.
To take a risk;
not to my demise,

like Liam tried to do,
but to ride the updraft
of holy love.

The frostbiting truth
was that I hadn't trusted God.
Still, He had come
through for me.
He rescued me like He rescued Freesia.
Only, I was so busy praying for Freesia,
too prideful to believe
I needed Him just as much.

Ma Moore once told me she survived
her *wildling years*
on prayers prayed
by her parents and grandparents,
aunts and uncles.
I thought,
Then I'll never survive…
with Daddy dead
and Mom not praying,
no grandparents at all—
well, except Ma Moore—
no aunts,
no uncles.
I remembered wanting not to survive.

But after Liam jumped,
when I couldn't see Freesia change
and Ma Moore didn't give me a verse,

277

the maybe of not wanting to survive
became certainty.

Ma Moore's prayers
bolstered me—
they must have—
when Liam might have died
and Freesia refused to accept Christ
and all I wanted was to give up.

Ma Moore said,
Prayers ascend as wishes
and return to us—
granted, postponed, amended, denied,
but heard.
All I really needed to know
was that God heard me
and would guide me
toward what was best for me.

I believed that.

Mom told Freesia
that family love
is like a bank account,
a series of debits and credits.
The sign of a successful family
is one with an abundant balance.

Now we have eleven account holders
to fill it jointly.

We maxed out on blessings
rained down from the prayers
of people like Daddy's mom
and Ma Moore,
and now we're praying together
for ourselves and one another.

The night of Amie's birthday,
we had a hot fudge sundae contest
at Aunt Sonya and Uncle Phil's.

In the kitchen,
while we waited to make ours,
Liam and I stood behind the other kids,
holding hands.

The Littles worked hard
to make their sundaes
without making messes.
Aunt Sonya was a staunch stickler
for cleanliness and tidiness.
A woman after Freesia's own heart!

When the Littles moved
to the table with their creations,
and Liam and I advanced to step up
to the counter,
Uncle Phil and Uncle Garyth
jumped in front
of us,
grabbed the bowls

right out of our hands,
and laughed—
Me first! We're next!
—little kids in big men's bodies.

They piled their sundaes high
while singing some corny song
about lovebirds
and making obnoxious kissing noises with their lips.

Liam rolled smiling eyes—
a glow and a grin
that were way overdue.
Almost an entirely different boy
than the afflicted soul
I first laid eyes on,
a stranger to the one
who thought himself worthless.

After stuffing our faces
and Azalea being dubbed the winner
by some arbitrary scale
that Uncle Garyth made up,
Amie wanted to go to Spriggs Park
to play frisbee.
We piled into three cars.
By the time we got there,
the sky has gone
from azure to slate.
Thunder, less threatening
than the chihuahua next door

who growls every time we walk by,
grumbled empty.

We eleven fell out of three cars
carrying water bottles,
sunscreen we wouldn't use,
three frisbees.
Dahlia and Azalea ran to the playground.

Mom, now lithe
with feathery
salt and pepper kinks
surrounding her head like
a Native American headdress,
shouted for someone to throw a frisbee to her.

We passed and caught,
dove and jumped,
teased and laughed,
all the while subconsciously
glancing at the sky.

Although we'd had warning,
the buckets of water
capsized,
astonishing us.
We screamed and crouched,
gathered our things
drenched in frenzy.
Mom called
to Dahlia and Azalea,

281

who were already running.

There was an unspoken
understanding
that whichever car
made it back to the house first
would get the leftover ice cream and toppings.
Liam and I claimed Uncle Garyth
as our driver
before anyone else could
because he sped
a tiny red sports car and would get back first.

Liam crouched in the back.
Uncle Garyth drove
me in shotgun.

And then it happened.
We passed through a wall
like glass
where the rain ceased
and the sun declared itself.
Above us a rainbow
so audacious,
you could read its mind.
You know
it knows
it's a promise from God
as immutable
as the rest of His promises.
All of them

falling like rain
or emerging imperceptibly
like dew
or spanning in glory
like rainbows
or radiating energy
like the sun.
In whatever form we need them,
but sometimes too subtle
for us to recognize
right away
or ever.
Our brains so insufficient.
His all so vast.

I turned around in my seat and saw
the other two cars,
still being pummeled.

I understood
for the first time
that God is just,
but He is not fair.
He gives individually,
according to need.

When it rained last year
for only them,
rain was not being withheld
from us
unjustly.

We faced a drought
and came out stronger
in Him,
in one another,
in ourselves.
The drought was necessary
to bolster us against future storms
and so we could appreciate the rain.

It was a mad dash to the house,
but our car won.
We piled in,
soaked,
but even Aunt Sonya wasn't worried
about the wet and outside
that we tracked in.
There was enough of everything leftover
for everyone.

The uncles disappeared for an hour
and came back with two Schnoodle puppies.
Liam chose the parti-colored pup,
an ivory female
with two big black spots on her back
and one covering the left side of her face.
Three of her paws
had speckled black polka dots.

Liam named his girl HatTrick.
Three can be a really good number, Eye.
I avoided three of anything at all costs,

and he teased me about my superstition.

Because it was her birthday,
Amie got to name our pup.
You'd think he was all grey if you didn't look close enough
to see the faint white stripe that shot straight down
his underbelly
from his chin to his tail.
Daddy told me once that if I'd been a boy, I would be Aster.
So that's what she named him.

The evening was full
of laughter,
with the occasional bicker
over the puppies
sprinkled in for moderation.
It became clear to Liam that when the Littles were around,
HatTrick was theirs, too.
Dahlia insisted on calling her *Cow*,
so she always answered to either name.

For us and the Glenns,
life became
happier-ever-after.

Of course we sisters
still occasionally wreaked
the harshest silent treatment
on one another as ever was imposed.

But then we'd laugh again,
unbridled in our love.

Our house was a torrent of
musical chatter—
gleeful
or angry—
uninhibited dancing,
slammed doors
(only if Mom wasn't home),
borrowed without asking
clothes and shoes
and, once or twice,
money.
Constant uprisings
of bribes and negotiations
for chores left undone
and chores doubled up.
Secrets shared and
secrets snooped out.

We were tumbleweed,
brown limbs and dark hair,
rebelliously blown by our own volition
if we were not careful,
if we did not steadfastly live out
our faith in God.

Striving to be led.
Repeatedly stumbling.
Endlessly repentant.

But, mostly,

we reminded me of Ma Moore's last verse,
the one she'd written after her signature.

Then our mouths were filled with laughter and our tongues with joyful songs. Then the nations said, "The LORD has done spectacular things for them. The LORD has done spectacular things for us. We are overjoyed.

—Psalm 126:2–3

ABOUT THE AUTHOR

Joiya Morrison-Efemini is the author of The Notes They
Played, a lyrical collection of short stories that croon to
the tune of change, loss, companionship, and finding
one's way through the dark, and The Impossible, a
historical novel, loosely based on the life of her
grandparents who left Georgia and settled in New York
in the Great Migration. She lives in Marietta, Georgia with
her husband, four children, a cat named Gia, and a
phantom Schnoodle named Deuce. If she's not running
her house, running her kids around town, or running
miles with her girlfriends, you'll likely find her curled up
with a good book. More on Joiya and her work can be
found at

www.joiyamewrites.com

CPSIA information can be obtained
at www.ICGtesting.com
Printed in the USA
LVHW020705260720
661550LV00008B/171

9 781947 327825